THE BIG FIFTY

This Large Print Book carries the
Seal of Approval of N.A.V.H.

THE BIG FIFTY

JIM MILLER

WHEELER PUBLISHING
An imprint of Thomson Gale, a part of The Thomson Corporation

Detroit • New York • San Francisco • New Haven, Conn. • Waterville, Maine • London

LIBRARY OF CONGRESS CATALOGING-IN-PUBLICATION DATA

Miller, Jim, 1945–
  The big fifty / by Jim Miller.
    p. cm. — (Wheeler Publishing large print western) (The long guns series)
  ISBN-13: 978-1-59722-517-5 (lg. print : pbk. : alk. paper)
  ISBN-10: 1-59722-517-7 (lg. print : pbk. : alk. paper)
  1. Large type books. I. Title.
PS3563.I4125B54 2007
813'.54—dc22   2007003698

Published in 2007 by arrangement with James L. Collins.

Printed in the United States of America on permanent paper
10 9 8 7 6 5 4 3 2 1

This one's for Phil Smith at the V.A.,
for knowing the difference
between *education* and *intelligence.*

CHAPTER 1

I've been in trouble all my life.

Sometimes I think I'm cursed with it.

When I walked into the Long Branch that day, I knew it for a fact. Not that trouble followed me *everywhere,* you understand. It's just that some people come into your life and, like it or not, they set you on your ear. And I spotted two of them right then, as soon as my eyes adjusted to the darkness. There at the table, sharing a drink and some conversation, were Hard Luck Hank and Sis. As soon as I saw them, I was going to duck out and leave — the saloon, the city, maybe even the territory! I just didn't think I could stand being with either one of them again, much less with both of them together.

"Guns!" Hank yelled out, seeing me. "Have a drink." He waved me on over to the table.

Strange as it may seem, that's my name. Guns. Well, not really. Actually, it's Matthew Hooker, and even that's not my *real* name. "Guns" is sort of a nickname I picked up way back when I was thirteen and damn near busted my wrist shooting Grandpa's old Walker Colt. With one hand. Everyone thought it was funny, so I got determined and learned how to shoot every gun I could get my hands on. And Guns is what they've called me ever since.

Guns Hooker. Sometimes it gets to be a hell of a name to live with.

I ambled over to the table, taking notice of a few other buffalo hunters seated in the establishment. Actually, you couldn't really call it an establishment, but it was spring of '74 now and the people who lived in town had decided to fancy the place up. They had even changed the name from Buffalo City to Dodge City. The idea was that it would sound more respectable and bring in a "better class of people," an expression I had grown to hate.

"Give us another beer!" Hank yelled to the barkeep as I tried to fit my oversized frame into the chair. I had hope that someday they would build chairs for bigger men like me. I set the Big Fifty, my Sharps buffalo rifle, against the table next to me. When the beer came, I drank half of it on one pull, then set it down for sipping just to be neighborly.

"Well now, what are you doing here?" It was Hank, trying to sound friendly. Damn, but he tried hard at that. It just didn't seem he could make friends worth spit. He couldn't have been more than twenty-five, and he wasn't particularly bad-looking or anything. It was just that he had the hardest luck of anyone I'd ever seen! And what made it worse was that he tended to spread it around to those with him.

"I might ask you the same thing," I said, taking both of them in.

"I work here, Matt, remember?" Sis had these big brown eyes that matched her hair, and along with the way she was talking, real infatuated-sounding and all, why, it didn't take a body long to see what was in those eyes. The woman was in love, and unfortunately, it was *me* she had fallen in love with! Oh, she was a beauty all right, all of twenty years old and full of innocence. But I wasn't the marrying kind. Besides, I was pushing forty now, and that could be old if you let it.

"Starting early, or are you working double shift?" I asked, taking a more-than-casual gander at the skimpy costume and fishnet stockings she wore. She was one of a handful of girls who served drinks in the Long

Branch, and it surprised me that no one had proposed marriage to her yet. Were I younger, I might have just done that, for when Cissy — that was some fancy back-East name she laid claim to, but I called her Sis — well, when she leaned forward over the table like she was doing now, all I could think of was how . . . *healthy* she was. Lordy, was she healthy!

"I wanted to look my best for you, Matt," she said with that same moo-cow look in her eyes. Oh, she was an attention getter all right. She had my attention so completely that I didn't even see what happened next until it happened. One second she was there, and then she was gone, yanked right out of her seat.

"Come on, cutey, you and me got some business to transact." She was standing now, and at the far end of her right arm, holding her wrist, was the beefy fist of Lance Carver, another buffalo hunter. He was also a cheat and a thief, although no one had been able to prove it so far, and many of the other hunters didn't have the guts to confront the man with such an accusation. Likely because he was big and mean and liked to advertise it.

"Let go of her," I said. I wasn't about to get excited over either one of them, the man or the woman, but what he had just done, well you didn't do stuff like that on the frontier and get away with it. And Carver had been getting away with it for too long. I finished my beer and pushed back my chair but remained seated.

"You let go of me, you bully," Sis was saying. It didn't take much to hear the fear in her voice. "Matt is my man," she added, though I wasn't sure if she actually meant it or was only trying to scare Carver.

"No, I'm not," I said, getting up. I noticed Hank cautiously rise from his seat, too, beer in hand. Then I saw his look of caution turning to one of anticipation, and I had the notion that things weren't going to work out quite the way I hoped.

"Just let her go, Carver. Hell, it ain't even suppertime yet." I took a step toward him, and a big one it was too.

"Well, if she ain't yours, then she mought's well be mine." He said it with all the meanness he was known for, just pushing as far as he could. It was clear he had a purpose in it, but I still didn't know what it was other than pure meanness.

"No, she ain't yours, either. Now let go of her." I didn't want to fight; I really didn't. But he sure must have wanted to, because he only squeezed the girl's wrist that much harder, producing a squeal of pain from Sis, at the same time he grabbed my shirt with his free fist.

"What are you gonna do about it?"

"Please, Matt, make him let go. He's hurting me," Sis wailed.

"That's a new shirt," I said. I could feel the mad coming out in me, and I knew then it just wasn't going to be settled peacefully.

He yanked down on the first button and muttered, "Not now it ain't," as the little piece of metal bounced to the floor. Mind you now, I never have cared for plug uglies like Carver, and no man worth his salt would stand by and let a woman be treated the way he was treating Sis. But what tore it was that button, because, friend, you don't rip nothing of mine apart lest I tell you to! Damn it, things are just too hard to come by these days! And when you make me angry, you pay the price. Carver began paying right then and there.

I hit him. Hard. In the gut.

He let out a grunt about the same time as he loosened his grip on my shirt and on Cissy's arm. She moved away, a frightened look still on her face, and I brought the heel of my boot down on the instep of Carver's foot. This time he let out a yell and straightened up to fight me. I grabbed him by his

12

own shirt front as he did, taking a step back. By the time I got a look at his ugly face, I saw he had an open space where a tooth used to be and decided I'd make him twice as ugly before I was through with him. I drove my right fist straight forward three times, punching his head back each time like it was one of those fancy punching bags they use back East. His eyes bulged out and his mouth fell open and I knocked out two more of his teeth before he fell backward and hit the floor unconscious.

Carver was a big man, but I stand well over six feet, and I outweighed him by forty pounds. It's at moments like this that I have sometimes regretted being big, because it draws people to you. No one normal, you understand. People who think they want to take you on. And all I wanted to be was left alone. But Carver had friends, and a couple of them were there in the saloon. One was making his way toward me as I was looking to see how Sis was doing. She now stood over on the far side of the table we'd been sitting at, out of harm's way, and that made me feel some better. What bothered me was the mischievous look in Hank's eye. Carver's friend was coming toward the table, when Hank threw the contents of his beer glass in the man's face!

"What did you do that for?" It seemed that both I and the other fella blurted it out at the same time. But it was the other man Hank heard.

"It's his beer," he said with a smile, pointing to me.

I reckon some people are about as empty as Aunt Martha's root cellar at the end of winter if you could look into what's above their neck. And there's people like Hank who sort of help them along. Anyone else would have popped Hank atwixt the eyes, but this fella just got reminded that it was me he was after in the first place.

He took a wide swing, and I caught his fist in my own, held it in mid-air, and started talking as mad as I felt.

"You *don't* want to do that, mister."

Then someone busted a chair across my back, and I went sailing forward into my opponent as he drove his free fist into my stomach. I brought my forehead down on the bridge of his nose and my knee up into his crotch just afterward, and he let out a yell like a wild banshee as he fell to the floor, both hands covering his elsewheres.

"Mister, that *hurt,*" I said, having some trouble turning to my rear. The man behind me should have called it quits and left while he could, but he thought he was going to have some more fun with me as he reached for a bottle of whiskey, only to have the barkeep grab it away before he could get to it. The man had his back against the bar now, a look of fear quickly rising to his face as he realized he was cornered. He was about to say something, when I hit him on the jaw with a roundhouse punch. Maybe he was play-acting, he went down so fast, but whatever the case, he'd have one hell of a sore face when he came to.

"Are you all right, Matt?" Sis said, rushing to my side. I flinched as she threw her arms around me, and thought for a minute I would pass out.

"Gimme that bottle," I said to the bartender, then took a good long swig of its contents. I set it down gently, waiting for the fire to take hold inside. I had to have something to kill the pain, for that chair had done a bit of damage to my back, even as thick and big-boned as I was. "Nothing a new rib won't cure," I said under my breath.

Suddenly it struck me that there was something vaguely familiar about what had just happened, something odd. But I couldn't pinpoint it. In the mirror above the bar, I could see Hard Luck Hank standing next to the entrance of the saloon and remembered the fun he seemed to have had adding to my troubles this afternoon. Then I didn't have the desire to do much other than get my hands on his scrawny neck.

He was looking out the batwing doors when I grabbed him and spun him around and put the fingers of one big hand around his neck, pinning him to the wall. He began to sputter and turn just a shade purple as his eyes bulged out and he pointed to the door.

"Guns," he said hoarsely when I eased up my hand some. "I wonder what that fella's doing with your horse out there."

CHAPTER 2

I looked over my shoulder, and by God, he was right! Now I'd been in enough fights and had cornered enough men to know that distraction was as good a way of staying alive for at least one more minute as any other. And I wouldn't have put it past Hank to try it either, as mad as I was, but the kid was telling the truth, for I saw the tail end of what he'd just described. Some fellow was running away from my horse or one of the horses on either side of it. . . . Hell, it was hard to tell.

I let go of Hank's throat, heard him sigh with relief as I did, and turned to head for my mount to see just what it was that had been done to him.

Except I didn't get far.

"Oh, Matt!" Sis said as I stopped nearly the same instant I tried moving. I don't know if she saw the grimace on my face, but I sure did *feel* it!

"Does it really hurt that bad?" She was there at my side trying to act like Florence Nightingale, not realizing until she did it that throwing her arms around me would only make the pain that much worse.

" 'Fraid so, Sis." I'd lost sight of the hombre that had gotten so skittish near my horse all of a sudden but did remember the fight that had just taken place and what I had been about to do to Hank. A scowl come over my face again as I slowly moved my shoulder around in its socket, feeling the pain it generated. "Someone hand me my Sharps," I said to no one in particular. But it was Hank I was staring at, and if he didn't know what I was thinking then, by God, he was as ignorant as he was unlucky!

"Gee, Guns, I didn't mean for it to turn out this way," he said in as humble a voice as you've ever heard. "I was just —"

"Having fun at my expense," I said, knowing that if I could move like I usually could just then, I'd likely have broken him in half. "Well, it's not funny, Hank, not at all." Someone handed me the Sharps, and I turned to leave, only half-aware that Sis was helping me out the door. But before I left, I added, "You just stay away from me, Hank. Go peddle your hard luck somewhere else."

He had the look of a newborn pup that's

been kicked in the gut and ain't sure what it's supposed to mean but only knows that it hurts. I didn't know if Hank had pulled that prank for show or if it was out of meanness, but I didn't really care either way, the condition I was in.

I didn't really know much about Hard Luck Hank, not even his real name. But then, nobody else did either, and if they were satisfied, then so was I. He'd just showed up that spring about the time the rest of us buffalo hunters had, claiming to be a skinner for hire to whoever could use one. I hadn't paid much attention to his name before or to any superstitions that might go along with it, but you can bet I was giving it serious thought as I strode down the boardwalk just then. Real serious thought.

"Say, where are you taking me?" I asked, looking down at Sis. I was so consumed with hatred for Hank and the man Carver that I'd forgotten just where I was going now that I'd left the saloon.

"Why, up to my room, Matt," she said with the kind of smile you see on the face of a woman who's ready to lower the hammer on you like a blacksmith trying to temper a piece of steel to his liking.

"Your room!" I must have nearly yelled it,

for it drew some awful strange glances from more than a couple of people on the streets. Your private life was your private life in those days, and that meant it was supposed to be, well, private. Besides, I'd been in places where all you had to do was be *seen* on the streets with a single woman and the townfolk figured that you had marriage on your mind, and that just wasn't true in this case. So I lowered my voice some when I said, "What do you mean, *your room?*" Maybe saying it through grit teeth would make her get the message.

"Well, it's only half a block away, Matt. And I've got some medicinals and such." She was being too sweet and kind for me to believe her. "On the other hand, if you'd like to walk or ride to that shack you call a home on the other side of town . . ." She let it trail off, knowing full well that I was in no shape to do either one at the moment.

"All right," I said, "but you get this straight, young lady. All you're gonna do is patch up these busted ribs and nothing else, you understand?"

She smiled and said, "Of course," in that tone a woman will use that lets you know she's going to have her own way no matter what you say. We walked the rest of that block in silence.

She must have made some kind of arrangement with the hotel to keep a room like the one she had, for as fancy as the lace on the bed was, she certainly wasn't paying for it out of what she made working at the Long Branch. On the other hand, some of those girls made a decent wage at that sort of work, even more than a cowhand sometimes. Seeing the inside of that room for the first time, I began to think that maybe Sis wasn't as innocent as she . . . No, I thought again, nobody could stand to be that mushy after they'd gotten over the innocent stage of life.

I didn't mind her taking my shirt off and pouring me a good stiff drink of hard liquor from what must have been her private stock, for the pain was still there and I had to have something to numb the feeling in my side. Besides, it wasn't bad stuff, this private stock. When she disappeared for about ten minutes to get some hot water, I sat on that bed of hers and gave a brief going-over to what had just happened.

Like I said, that whole incident in the saloon and the way it had happened just didn't seem right. Not that I wouldn't have put it past Hard Luck Hank to set up such a fight, for he was a mischievous one when he wanted to be — I'd seen that in his eyes when he'd thrown the beer in that second fellow's face. The fight had just given me one of those eerie feelings you get once in a while. You know what I mean, the kind that tells you for one split second that you've been there before one way or another. But that was all beyond me.

Sis came back shortly with her hot water and that frantic look a body gets when they're busting to tell you the latest gossip. And she was.

"Do you know what happened while you were fighting for my honor?" she asked excitedly. I cringed then, knowing full well I hadn't been fighting for her honor as much as I had been trying to mind my own business.

"Beats the hell outta me," I said. At least she could do two things at one time and took to patching up my side as she let me in on the news that there'd been a robbery in town. Not that it hadn't happened before, you understand, for this was still a wild town.

"The new jewelry store down the street was the one broken into." She was applying the liniment with as much vigor as she was telling her story, and I felt it. "They're saying the thieves took a whole bunch of valuable rings and such!"

"Maybe that'll teach 'em not to keep that kind of thing on hand. That's about as careless as having a payroll shipment come into the bank without an armed guard to watch over it."

She shrugged, and all of a sudden the subject changed.

"If you say so, Matt," she said with that moon-eyed look about her again. Now friend, I ain't going to say that when you're pushing forty from the north side, you ain't enjoyed the company of a woman or two in all those years, not at all. But when you get to be that age, you either get ready to settle down or become a confirmed bachelor of sorts, knowing that you'll never do much good for any woman who's looking for a decent man to make a life with. So when a woman takes to getting serious about me . . . well, it's time to move on, for the thought of being chained to one place purely scares the hell out of me! Don't get me wrong, I liked Sis, or Cissy or whatever her fancy back-East name was. Hell, there were times I could even put up with Hard Luck Hank. But . . .

I shouldn't have been thinking that much. It never was my long suit. Maybe if I'd been standing, I'd have had a chance, but sitting there on her bed just about eye-level with her healthiness caught me off-guard. Sis quick-like took both of her hands, laid them upside my face, and leaned over and kissed me real hard. It was so hard, in fact, that it pushed me back down on the bed, and she was acting like she didn't want to let go. For a minute there neither did I. It must have been a long while since I'd had a woman's company, for I didn't even notice the pain that having her atop me was making in my side. I reckon my attention was elsewhere. Then I remembered that look she'd had in her eyes, and the scared came back to me, knowing what I'd be getting myself into if I kept up what I was doing. I grabbed hold of the far side of her hip and gently rolled her off me as I struggled to get to a standing position.

"Doctoring only, remember?" I tried to say it as sternly as I could, but it was hard to do as she stood now, too, looking at me with that pleasing smile of hers.

"But you did like it, Matt, didn't you? You know, I really do love you."

"Well . . . sure I liked it." If honesty was what she wanted, then that's what she'd get, whole-hog. "I'd be lying to you if I said I didn't." I paused, trying to gather the right words. "But I'd be lying just as much if I said I was in love with you, Sis, 'cause I ain't."

"But Matt —" The hurt was crawling up into her face the way I figured it would, and if that was how a broken heart felt, I didn't want anything to do with it. Still, she had to know the truth.

"Any other man would have liked it just as well, Sis, for you're a beautiful woman." I shrugged, giving her what was a weak smile at best; I didn't want to hurt her, but I knew I would. "Trouble is, I don't think you're past puppy love yet. Besides, I'm not the marrying kind, and . . ." It just sort of trailed off into a dead-end canyon, because what I was about to say next would hurt both of us.

"And what?" She was trying to be some kind of brave soldier now, but the tears were rolling down her cheeks, making her speech barely audible.

"And," I said, clearing my throat and sloshing on my hat as I grabbed the Sharps and headed for the door, "I'm old enough to be your father." You talk about feeling pain! I had to get out of there before my words wound up doing us both in. I didn't know if she heard what I said next, for she had fallen onto the bed, burying her head in the fancy bedspread, crying her heart out.

"It just wouldn't work," I said, and left.

The patch-up job Sis had done was first-rate, and between it and the liquor I'd consumed since the fight, I had a notion I'd be able to walk — slowly, to be sure — to my horse and see if I couldn't make it back to what I was calling home and get some rest. I hate to say I used the Sharps for a cane walking that block back to my mount, and it was likely the first time the populance had seen me carry the gun in that manner.

Cissy was right about the place I hung my hat being just shy of what you'd call a shack, because that's just what it was. A small one-room abode barely big enough to keep me and whatever I decided I wanted to keep from getting wet during the spring rains. Blow away if a good wind came along, that's what it would do.

I unsaddled the mount and took the riggings inside, leaving the door open for some light. Might as well check to see if I had all my gear just in case that pilgrim I'd seen earlier had been trying to swipe something when I spotted him. It all looked in order until I dug into one of my saddlebags to gather my cleaning equipment and such for the Sharps. That was when I found it.

"Jesus, Mary, and Joseph!" was all I could say when I saw it.

Hard Luck Hank had been right about someone fooling with my horse, except it wasn't with my horse. Whoever it was hadn't been taking when he had been in my saddle-bags — he'd been *putting.*

I sat there just staring at it, not believing what I was seeing! It looked to be near as big as my thumb. And considering what Sis had said about a hold-up of the local jewelry store, well, things started to fall into place, and it wasn't long before I knew it was one of the items stolen in the robbery.

But I got to tell you, hoss, that didn't stop me from staring at it, for it sure did look to be the biggest diamond I'd ever seen!

CHAPTER 3

Now, if you think I was going to turn over that diamond to the local law and wind up going to jail for being in on the holdup, why, you're crazy! Maybe I should have gone to the sheriff, but the buffalo-hunting season was starting pretty soon and, well, I wasn't about to miss that. So after a considerable bit of thinking, I decided I'd find the fellow who planted this piece in my saddlebags and turn *him* in. Trouble was, I'd gotten only a brief glimpse of him as he fled, and that was going to make it hard to find him.

Being in pain never stopped your stomach from letting you know when it was time to be fed, and mine was doing that to me, so I walked about a block or so to the nearest eatery. It wasn't the best, but it was the closest, and that was important right then. There was a bit too much grease on the fried potatoes that came with the steak I ordered, and the bread was nothing like Ma used to make when we were kids, but the coffee was hot and strong, and that sort of makes up for what the grub lacks in taste. Well, sometimes.

That diamond wasn't in my saddlebag anymore either. I'd hidden it elsewheres so it would be safe just in case whoever it was that robbed the jeweler decided they wanted it back. And as greedy as men are, I figured that he — or they — would do just that.

Moving about is the best you can do for some bruises, lest they turn and get more painful and stiff than you'd like them to be, so I decided to make the rounds of some of the saloons just to be doing something. Besides, I might get a gander at the fellow I'd seen earlier — if he hadn't lit a shuck.

There were a goodly number of gambling halls, saloons, and dens of iniquity in general in Dodge City then, and you could get lost in any one of them once business picked up in the late evenings. But I was only going to stop in at a few of the better watering holes. Hell, if the man who stole that diamond had that good taste for jewelry, he'd likely not settle for some of the cheap home-brew whiskey that was served in this town.

Fat Jack's was the first place I stopped at. Fat Jack was the barkeep who ran the place, a man who was sort of a contradiction in terms, so to speak. You see, no one had ever put a sign on the front of his place, but the name it was called didn't bother Jack at all, I reckon, for he never made mention of it. And Jack wasn't exactly fat, either. Oh, he was tending to a gut, but I knew of no one who'd want to run across him in a side alley, be it day or night, and that included me. For other than that paunch he was pure muscle.

"Heard you was in another fight today, Guns," he said, setting up a glass and a bottle of whiskey in front of me.

"Yeah." I tossed off the drink, felt it burn its way down to my gut, and knew Jack was trying out a new recipe for mixing together the cheaper brands of whiskey he served. When I got my voice back, I said, "Times I wonder if the whole world ain't out to get me, Jack, especially when I drink this rotgut of yours. Why not give me a decent drink."

He smiled and took the bottle away, replacing it with another. He leaned closer to me as he poured the liquor.

"You hear how much them fellers got away with in that jewelry store robbery this afternoon?" He was acting like it was all sort of hush-hush and secret, which didn't make a whole hell of a lot of sense to me.

"No" — I shrugged — "just that they took off with some —" I paused a moment, realizing that no one had really told me just what it was these characters had made off with. "Say, Jack, what is it that they took?"

"Thousands of dollars' worth of gems, they're saying." If he was as astonished as he sounded, I'd be surprised, for Fat Jack wasn't the astonishable type. "Plenty of stones, they're saying."

"Jack, do you realize that if we could ever find out who *they* are, we'd be able to solve half the problems in this world?" I took another drink as the big man frowned, lost by what I'd said. "I never did put much faith in *them,* whoever they are, Jack . . . unless, of course, you'd happen to know."

"Well, uh . . . they, uh . . . the owners, I guess." He wasn't astonished now at all, rather acting a bit bewildered instead. He looked about, frowned, and lowered his voice to me. "Look, Guns, you keep this to yourself, you understand?" Jack knew I would, but the look on his face was the murderous kind I'd seen before only when someone had tried to make a day's work out of breaking up Jack's bar, except that the fellow had gotten cut off at the knees in about ten minutes and never was heard from again.

31

"You know me better than that."

His face turned into a frown as he shifted his eyes left, then right to see who-all was there, and he began pouring me another drink. The whiskey was good but powerful, and suddenly I was finding myself glad that those potatoes had been on the greasy side, for I'd likely need as much absorption as I could get before the night was over.

"You know Asa, the fella runs the store?" Jack asked.

I shrugged and shook my head. "Got no use for jewelry."

"Well, he's my brother-in-law. I ain't too awful fond of him my own self, Guns, but I told my sister I'd keep an eye on him." Then that murderous look came to Jack's face again. "What I really oughtta do is kill the little runt."

"You feel that way about an in-law?" I've always been more interested in the pasture off yonder than I ever was in my own backyard, so what Fat Jack was saying sort of threw me.

"Never get hitched, Guns!" he said in his normal booming voice. It got the attention of those in the bar, whether he intended it to or not. "And if you do get the urge, make sure you marry an ugly woman!"

"An ugly one?" The way he was carrying

on had me a mite confused.

"Why, of course! That way, when she leaves you, you won't feel like you're losing anything." That comment drew a laugh from most of the drinkers, who seemed to agree with Jack, giving him a round of applause. While Jack was taking his bow, I made a mental note to mention his advice to Sis the next time she tried to get me in her clutches.

"When you get through entertaining the customers, Jack, maybe you can tell me about your brother-in-law and his store."

"Oh, yeah." He slowly poured me another drink and lowered his voice. "Least the rest of the place figures we're talking 'bout my relatives."

"I see." Well, we were.

"Asa wanted me to keep my ears open and see if I could find out anything 'bout the jewels he lost. Why, he had one that's big and shiny and oughtta bring at least a thousand dollars!"

That would be the diamond I'd found. I was glad I'd hidden it in as safe a place as I had.

"Wish I could help you, Jack." I sipped my drink. "How many was it Asa said pulled the job?"

"He's saying three."

"Hope the law catches up with 'em." I tossed off the drink and grabbed up the Sharps to go. But not before Fat Jack threw in one last insult about his brother-in-law.

"Do you know how useless Asa is? Why, he'd blow his brains out trying to clean a pistol, he's that dumb!"

"Good thing he stuck with jewelry," I said as I left.

I spent another hour or so dropping in at the better saloons in the next couple of blocks. The liquor was warming to me, but I still had my wits about me as I continued my search for the man I'd seen earlier in the day. After the conversation with Fat Jack, I found myself being a bit more cautious in my looking, not sure I could deal with all three of those hombres at one time.

It was the end of that second block I thought I saw the man in one of the saloons. Fact is I walked right up to an open space next to him at the bar.

"Nice evening," I said.

"Yeah" was his only reply, but he didn't even glance my way.

"Say, don't I know you?" One way or another I was determined to get his attention. I straightened up when he looked my way and both of us saw something in each other's face. It must have been recognition he saw in mine, for a look of fear and caution came to his.

"No, you don't know me," he said, finishing his drink and making his way toward the saloon entrance.

I followed him, not as quickly as I should have, perhaps, but one fight a day was enough. It was only some fifty feet to the alley I saw him duck into and the sun was nearly down, so I held the Sharps in both hands in the position soldiers call port arms. I'd paid good money for that gun and wasn't about to lose it out of carelessness.

I hadn't finished taking my first step past the open alley when a fist came flying out at me, meant for my face. What stopped it was the end of my Sharps. He gave a short cry, and I did a forty-five-degree turn and planted the butt of that Sharps square into his side, knowing he'd feel as bad off as I did. It was too dark to make out his features, but I didn't have time anyway. All I knew was he wasn't the man I'd followed out of the saloon.

The one I'd followed stepped right out in front of me while I was doing in his partner and stuck his pistol into my front. Now, hoss, that's a hell of a time to start thinking of your Maker, but I did, for this fellow was fixing to do me in on a permanent basis.

And he would have, too, if his pistol hadn't misfired! It must have been a cap 'n' ball, one of those Civil War makes, for all I heard was a click as the both of us started cussing at the same time. I reckon that's the only reason I'm the one telling this story instead of him. But he still had his pistol into me, and I knew that he'd succeed in killing me with his next try if I didn't do something quick. He was cocking his pistol when I brought the butt of that Sharps down on his wrist and knocked it out of his hand just before a burst of flame shot out of the barrel. When he turned to run, I brought the Sharps barrel down and threw a .50-caliber slug over his shoulder as he and his compadre made it to their horses and lit a shuck. And you can bet that Sharps drew a crowd, loud as it was.

The marshal made his way through the onlookers, and I had to explain that I'd been attacked by a couple of strangers, although I knew good and well I'd know one of them the next time I saw him. I don't know if it was the moving around or being scared that made me lose my wind, but I sure had.

When the crowd dispersed and the marshal had left, I decided I'd had my fill of poking around that night and slowly made my way back to my makeshift home, stopping only long enough to let Fat Jack know what had happened.

"If it was them thieves that I tangled with, you can bet they ain't in town anymore," I said.

"What about the pistol you knocked out of the man's hand?"

"An 1860 Colt's Army. There's thousands of 'em still in use."

When I got back to my home, well, it wasn't exactly my home anymore. Whoever it was that had done it hadn't needed much strength to tear the place apart, but they'd done a good job of it anyway. The walls, flimsy as they were, had been torn down and apart enough so I'd have a hard time rebuilding what little I did have. The contents of my saddle bags were strewn about, the riggings on my saddle cut a mite here and there. If it was a three-man operation that pulled that robbery Jack was talking about and I'd had a run-in with two of them, I'd sure enough wager that it was the third man who'd taken apart my living quarters — probably about the same time his friends were trying to take me apart.

"Weren't nothin' I cud do 'bout it, Mista Hooka." Turning around I saw Joshua, the tall somewhat skinny black man who worked nights at the livery next to what used to be my quarters. I'd made an arrangement with him to watch over my belongings if I wasn't around, throwing an extra five dollars his way at the end of the month for the service.

"I don't imagine so," I said, already seeing in my mind what must have happened. "He pull a gun on you?"

"Yessa," he nodded. "A big 'un."

I smiled. "Most of 'em are when you're looking down the business end. You know what kind it was?"

"A Walka? Maybe a dragoon. He had 'im a holsta fer it."

"Likely a dragoon. Ain't many men ever had the strength to carry a Walker by their side for too awful long. What'd he look like?"

"Tall. Strong. Busted that wood up like it twas toothpicks. Weren't no uglier'n half the men I see come 'n' go 'round here. I'd know 'im agin, though. You kin bet on dat."

"Good. You let me know if he crawls outta his hole again," I said.

"Yessa."

Joshua had a vacant stall and let me bed down in it. But before I called it a night, I made sure to clean my Sharps and see that it was loaded proper.

One good thing about growing up on the frontier is that you learn how to be your own handyman. More often than not you make your own clothes, catch and cook your own food, and mend your own tools, including your guns. In my case I'd also picked up a good bit of training in the carpentry field. By doing that, I'd gotten fairly decent at making stocks for rifles, too. Fact is, I'd made the one for the Sharps; and when I did, I fit in a shallow pocket like they used to put in some of the old Kentucky smooth bores to keep extra ball and patches in. I kept percussion caps in mine instead. To keep the metal cover in place, I'd fashioned a thick leather strap that encompassed the stock in that area, making sure the cover wouldn't open unless I bade it.

Joshua was a bit befuddled when I wasn't as outraged as he by the damage that had been done to my place but simply picked up the mess and placed my gear in the back stall. But I wasn't going to tell him that I knew whoever had done this hadn't found what they'd been looking for.

Like I always said, I wasn't about to give up my Sharps without a good fight, because it was an expensive gun to replace. But I had another reason as well. You see, the hideout I'd fashioned was where I'd hid the diamond.

CHAPTER 4

The stiffness I was feeling the next morning sort of dissuaded me from pursuing the outlaws I'd tangled with the day before. Besides, they could be a hundred miles away by now if they'd ridden their mounts into the ground like some desperate men did. So I only gave going after them a passing thought as I ate that morning and concentrated instead on finding another place to stay and on keeping my gear in shape for if and when word came that buffalo had been sighted to the south.

I'd been hunting for buffalo for a couple, three years now, and it was the same every year. The hunters, hiders, and outfitters would all gather in Dodge or the surrounding area and wait for word of some sighting down south before taking off like a bat out of hell to slaughter as many as we could. Depending on the season, you could get a dollar a hide or more once you got the hides back up to Dodge, and that wasn't bad pay when you consider that a crack shot could down a hundred to a hundred and fifty of those hairy beasts a day. And there was never a lack of meat, though there were many of us to feed at hunting time. So I figured that I'd spend a week or so patching up my gear and letting these old bones of mine heal proper before word came and the season opened. I also made a mental note to take real good care of the Sharps, for more than one reason.

Actually, the buffalo gun had quite a history to it, for it wasn't always a buffalo gun, you know. The Sharps had been around for a quarter of a century and had seen a goodly bit of use on more than just buffalo. When Christian Sharps first patented the weapon in 1848, you could get it in a short-barreled carbine or a rifle and load it with loose powder and ball or with a paper-wrapped cartridge and ball. You could say it was one of the first lever-action guns we ever had on the frontier, although a crude one in those early days. The trigger guard acted as a lever, making it easy to load the paper cartridge. The Sharps used a percussion cap, and in its own way, it sort of revolutionized the rifle, for a good man could get off four or five shots in one minute, which was near as good as the Colt's pistols and a damn sight better on range. And, like Colt's pistols and long guns, you could get the Sharps in a variety of calibers, ranging from .36 to .52. By the mid-1850s it was likely the most popular rifle west of the Mississippi and began to take on the nickname Old Reliable, it was that good.

It was during those years before the Civil War, the Bleeding Kansas days, that the Sharps got another nickname. It seems that old Henry Ward Beecher, a sky pilot abolitionist from back East, got so carried away with the thought of freedom that he claimed that one Sharps rifle would do more good against the proslavery folks than any hundred Bibles. The story goes that Beecher sent a crate full of Sharps rifles to John Brown out here in Kansas. The crate was stamped *Bibles,* and the rifles inside promptly became known as Beecher's Bibles by John Brown and his men. It was those Sharps that Brown and his men were carrying when they made that less-than-successful raid on Harpers Ferry in 1859.

Oh, the Sharps had its problems all right, gas leaking at the breech, parts that occasionally went afoul, and times when your bullet might lose velocity and accuracy, but it wasn't any different in that respect from other breechloaders of that day.

It was after the war when the railroads were being built that the Sharps gained a new popularity. Even with the appearance of the Henry, Spencer, and Winchester during and after the war, it was still the Sharps that the buffalo hunters turned to when it came to supplying one hell of a lot of meat to those lads working the rails. But it wasn't until 1869, when they drove that gold spike of the first U.S. transcontinental railway at Promontory Point up Utah way, that Sharps modified a goodly number of his weapons so they'd take the new metallic cartridges. There were a variety of different loads, but they were all .50-caliber, which, I reckon, led me and a bunch of the others to refer to this new Sharps as the Big Fifty. And you mark my word, friend. You'd have to go some to find a more accurate long gun for the range it gave. Why, hell, there's the story about . . . but that's another canyon.

It took only a couple of days of lazy work to get my gear back in shape before I was getting to feel restless again. It got that way for me every spring while we hunters waited for the buffalo to head north far enough so we could head south. But this year I had a notion things were going to be just a tad different. It was when Charlie Myers approached me that I knew for certain I was right. Don't ask me how. I just knew.

"You're pretty good with that long gun of yours, Guns," he said, squatting down to where I was finishing my mending. He wasn't particularly big as men go, but he was known for making some of the best sugar-cured, boneless hind-quarter buffalo meat in the state of Kansas. "How'd you feel about hiring on with me for an expedition I'm planning?"

"Expedition? No, no thanks, Charlie. I'll make my money buffalo hunting this spring."

"This ain't gonna cut into your buffalo hunting none," he said. "You'll still get it in, guaranteed." He sounded determined to hire me. The two lads he'd brought along with him had a determined look about them, too. They weren't but in their early twenties, and neither was any bigger than Charlie Myers, but remembering those two hombres I'd tangled with in the saloon and the ones in the alley made me want a good piece of ground to stand on. Just in case these two had ideas. So I stood up, towering over all three of them.

"These men are Billy Dixon and Bat Masterson," Charlie added, almost as if they knew my thoughts. "They're new, but they're good with their guns, and they've thrown in with me. I want you to honcho the outfit I'm putting together."

Then he went on to tell me how he figured the hunting around Dodge had pretty well played out and how he wanted to move his business to a better location. The location he had in mind was south of us, down in the panhandle area, where a good share of the buffalo hunting would likely be done.

"It'll be sort of a rendezvous area like the old mountain men had," he said, "except this will be strictly for you buffalo hunters. The way I figure it, I can give you men a lot easier access to the supplies and ammunition you'll need during the season."

Charlie Myers was a good man, so I had no reason to doubt his word, and if he said something would work out, it likely would.

"And you want me to honcho this operation?"

"That's right, Guns. I do the hiring and firing, and you point 'em in the right direction. I'll pay you a hundred dollars when we get there, and I'll supply you with the rounds for your Sharps. Sound fair?" He stuck out a paw to seal the deal and I took it.

"Why not?" I said, shrugging. "I never was much on city living."

It took Charlie another week to get his crew together, but by the time we left, he had a good fifty men and some thirty wagons to make the trek to wherever it was we were going to set up shop. True to his word, Charlie gave me a free hand in running this lash up, which sort of reminded me of that time Pa and my brother and I drove that herd of cattle out of Texas; but that was some years ago. I'd had more than my share of run-ins during that drive, but we'd been mostly dealing with muleheaded mavericks that time.

There was only once that I gave question to Charlie Myers's judgment in his picking of men, and that was when I saw Hard Luck Hank jawing with Carver, the bully I'd had the fight with, and his partner, the second man who'd gone after me in the Long Branch that day. Charlie was in sight, so I called him over as I approached the three men.

"You hire 'em?" I asked Myers. It was probably the first time I'd ever sounded curt with him.

"Well, yeah, I did. Hank here claims to be the best skinner in the state, and the other two —"

"They call him Hard Luck Hank, Charlie, and if he's the best at anything in this state, it's purely in his mind." Then I threw a hard glare at Carver and his friend. "And I *know* what these two are."

"You got no call —"

Charlie stepped in, placing a firm hand on Carver's chest. "Now you hold on, mister," he said. "I'm the one who hands out the pay here, and if you want yours, you'll keep your place." Then, turning to me, he added, "I told you, Hooker, I do the hiring and firing."

"As long as they know I'm the one givin' the orders on the trail, Charlie. As long as they know."

It was easy to see that Charlie Myers had other, much more important things on his mind, and his frustration showed when he spoke next. "Listen, you two," he said, addressing Carver and me, "I heard about some fandango you got into a while back, but if you're gonna work for me, you'll do well to forget it, understand?" Without waiting for an answer from either of us, he furrowed his brow and slowly waved a short, squat finger at us. " 'Cause if you don't, I'll fire the both of you." Then he was gone.

"So you're supposed to be running this outfit, huh?" Carver was back to sounding as gamey as ever now that Myers was gone, with a sneer on his face and all. But I wasn't

47

having any of it.

"That's right, Chingo," I said right back at him. Pa said that smiling can get you into a lot of trouble, claiming that was how Ma got her hooks into him. Me, I'd found out a few other things about it since Pa'd told us that as kids — like knowing that throwing a strange word at a person along with a crooked smile tends to shake them some, since they don't know exactly what it is that you mean. What I'd just said was having the desired effect on Carver; his face screwed up something fierce.

"What's 'Chingo' mean, Guns?" Sometimes you couldn't tell if Hank was just plain ignorant or if he was acting that way in order to pull some kind of prank on you, but since it was obvious that Carver wanted to know as much as he did, I told him.

"Well, Hank, that depends," I said, still smiling at Carver as I spoke, knowing he wasn't liking a bit of this. "You get down into Mexico, and it's got one meaning."

"Well, what's that, Guns?" Hank asked, a bit impatient his own self.

"Don't think I oughtta tell you, Hank. It'd take your virginity away." The would-be buffalo skinner let out a shy sort of chuckle, but Carver's neck was turning a slow shade of red. "On the other hand, I knew a fella once who claimed he'd been way far south of Mexico, and they had a different meaning for it down there."

"Can you tell me that one, Guns?" Hank asked.

"Nope." I was still smiling at Carver, letting him know I had the upper hand.

"How come?" Hank was getting frustrated now, the way a kid does who's wanting to act grown-up but ain't reached the hay and grass part of his life yet. "Gee, I wish somebody'd tell me something!" He even stomped his foot like a youngster would.

"Well, you see, Hank, that friend of mine never could quite figure out what Chingo meant himself. Fact is, nearest he could come was that it was a combination of two things. Partly, well, it was something you'd never mention in front of your mama, Hank. I'll guarantee you that." Of a sudden, my smile was gone, replaced by a hard look and an even harder voice, all directed at Carver. "The other part, he said, was pretty clear in its meaning. What it meant was that you were *a lying sonofabitch.*"

Hank might have been naive about a lot of things, but he could see trouble coming as quickly as anyone. He must have caught a glimpse of what I'd known would come to Carver's eyes when I said that last, for he

49

stepped back out of the way real quick-like.

Carver's partner had been standing to the rear and side of his friend. In a way that was good, for when Carver began reaching for his Colt's, I took one fast step to the side and stuck the barrel of my Fifty right into his brisket. His compadre was in line with him, directly to the rear.

"Don't do it, friend." It was too bad Joshua from the livery wasn't there to see it, because Carver was beginning to break out in a sweat. And if he didn't know he was dead meat if he made the wrong move, well, hoss, he must have been even dumber than Hank. As for Carver's friend, well, the man wasn't going to get into anything that Carver didn't start first.

"You know, Carver, I've heard it said that success is the size of the hole a man leaves after he's dead."

"What're you talking about?" he said, his fist still covering the butt of his Colt's. "You called me a liar!"

"I said I knew what you are." I pushed the Sharps into his belly some, forcing him backward to keep him off-balance. Hell, I knew I could die just as quickly as he could; I just didn't want him taking that notion into his mind. "The point is that if you or your friend come anywhere close to clearing leather . . . well, Charlie Myers is gonna be able to drive one of his freight wagons through both of you without touching either side. And they ain't gonna put your remains in nothing but that outhouse in back of you."

He frowned, not recalling an outhouse behind him at all, probably because there wasn't one. But his curiosity got the better of him, and it was that one quick glance over his shoulder that gave me the chance I needed. I brought the butt of that Sharps up and connected with a part of his jawline, sending him back into his partner, and they both tumbled to the ground.

"Guns, that wasn't fair!" Hank said, looking down at Carver, who was now unconscious.

"You've been reading too many dime novels, Hank." I smiled. "As long as I'm up here and he's down there, that's all that counts. You think about that when someone tries to take your life someday."

I took in the features of Carver's partner, seeing for the first time that he wasn't all that old, just worn some on the outside. The whole thing had shaken his confidence, if he'd had any at all, leaving him looking like a scared rabbit.

"I'll tell you something, sonny. You stick

with Carver and you'll wind up dead before the summer's over. That's a near guarantee. But whoever it is you partner with, you'd better be able to stand beside 'em, *not* behind 'em, 'cause if you don't, you'll never be worth a damn," I told him.

He was getting up now, and I wasn't sure if he was too shaken to say anything or if he was just shy. I knew he wouldn't pull anything and was about to turn to leave when I stopped.

"And kid?" I said.

"Yes, sir."

"You tell Carver that if he don't do as he's told in this outfit, I'll kill him."

"Yes, sir." If nothing else, I had gained the respect of this youngster, who couldn't be much older than Masterson or Dixon.

"And son?" I gave him a hard, cold look as I said it.

"Yes, sir."

"If that time comes, and you're with him, I'll kill you, too."

I was walking away when Hard Luck Hank caught up with me.

"Gee, that was great, Guns!"

"There's nothing great about dying, Hank. And just stay away from me, Hank. Just stay away."

"But Guns, I'm —"

I stopped and looked him square in the face. "The best skinner in Kansas? My eye, and Betty Martin!"

Then I left him there, sort of stupefied by his own lies.

No, this wasn't going to be an ordinary season.

CHAPTER 5

Either I'd taken some of the bite out of
Carver, which hardly seemed possible, as
mean as he was, or the man had decided to
wait for a more opportune time to try to do
me in again, for the few remaining days we
spent getting those wagons ready were
pretty tame. Half of them carried supplies
that Charlie Myers would be using to set up
at his new location, while the rest were
empty, except for half a dozen that carried
our ammunition. You'd have thought we
were going to war with as much weaponry
and ammunition as we were bringing, and
in a way I reckon we were.

Each man had a rifle and a pistol and usually a knife of some sort on him by the time
we left. Me, I had one of those cavalry-
model Colt's that had come out the year
before, the ones with the seven-inch barrel;
it set on my left hip in a holster I'd fashioned
myself. A bowie knife hung from my right

side, but it was the Big Fifty that I counted on for range and just plain killing power. Fact is, you wouldn't find a buffalo hunter who thought much different in those days. And if that description is one of a man going to war, well, you have to remember that anything directly south or southwest and up north of Kansas was hairy country to be going into because there were still a bunch of Indian tribes that didn't think much of the white man invading their land. So if we looked a bit overarmed, there was a damn good reason for it.

Most of the men were too tired at the end of a day of loading supplies to do much hoorahing at night. It was when we'd finally left that they got into the spirit of things, pulling out fiddles, harmonicas, and whatnot the first night on the trail. Couldn't blame them, really, for once we got into Indian territory, there'd be a sight more caution taken when night camp was made.

After we'd been out a few days, we started coming upon camps here and there of buffalo hunters who'd paired up and decided they'd be that much closer to the panhandle when the season began. Like many a man who spends his life alone before a small fire at night, these men were glad to hear all of the gossip and latest news we cared to tell them. Trouble was the poor devils had to listen to Hank and his questions galore and brash bragging about the native population.

"I'll bet there's a heap of Injuns hereabouts, ain't there?" Hank asked gleefully of one such hunter.

"Yup," the old-timer replied, giving Hank a curious gaze in the process. "Been a mite of 'em 'round fer some time, I hear. Why? You got kin 'mongst 'em?"

"Oh, no," Hank said, his eyes beginning to bulge with what could be described only as wanton desire, though without a woman attached to it. "Me and Guns and Bat, why, we come to kill us off a good share of buffalo and near all the Comanche nation! Yes, we have!" His enthusiasm was unbounded.

"I see," the man said. It seems the older some of these codgers get, the more able they are to keep a straight face at what would make any other man break into laughter. "Well, now, son, that's right ambitious. You, uh, you figgering to take 'em on all at once or one at a time?"

"Oh, it don't make no difference," the pilgrim replied in his best aw-shucks manner. "They ain't got a chance against us no way."

The buffalo hunter finished his coffee while Hank threw more tenderfoot questions at him, then excused himself, saying he had to talk to the others. I don't know what the others were told, but I do remember the old-timer walking over to me that night and starting a casual conversation about the drinking water in the area. When he brought up an alkalied hole we'd passed, I told him I knew of it and asked why he'd mentioned it in particular.

"Well, friend," he said, lowering his voice, "if I was you, I'd keep an eye on that lad over there." Nodding toward Hank, he said, "That boy's been to the wrong water hole once too often. Yes, sir, I do believe it's addled his brain."

"You've got to give Hank credit for one thing, Guns," Bat commented later on, smiling. "At least he can stretch the blanket."

"I know, Bat. Trouble is, he ain't even trying. We get hit by renegades out here, I got a feeling Hard Luck Hank is gonna need one helluva lot of mothering." I aimed a hard look in Hank's direction. "And between you and me, Bat, I ain't got the time or the inclination for it. Not a-tall."

It was about then that we slowed down considerably in our progress, hitting the soft sandy soil that was the beginning of what we called No Man's Land. Some called it the Neutral Strip, but what it was was a piece of land you couldn't grow nothing on. I'd met a sky pilot the year before, one of those circuit riders, who'd come through this land and agreed that it was "so barren the Devil couldn't even grow sin on it." And if God ever dropped any water on it, it must have been only because He couldn't find the outhouse.

If Carver was staying away from me, then so was Hard Luck Hank. It seemed a shame that the only way you could get anyone to take notice of what you had to say was to threaten them, but some people are hardheads from birth to death, I reckon. What surprised me was how the young kid who was Carver's partner sat down next to me one night and did his best to strike up a conversation and be as friendly as he could. At first I just ignored him, paying more interest to the meat on my plate than to anything else. He was full of small talk until he got around to what he really wanted to say.

"I ain't Carver's partner no more." He sort of blurted it out in that boyish way Hank often did, like he was proud of what he'd done and ought to get a pat on the back for it.

"Finally showed some smarts." I said it matter-of-factly, although I had to admit it made me feel a bit easier knowing that Carver was on his own now.

"I give some thought to what you said, Mister Hooker, and I reckon you were right. Partnering with Carver just wouldn't be healthy." At least the kid had a bit of humility in him and knew enough to admit when he was wrong. That was more that I'd ever gotten out of Hard Luck Hank. And maybe that was the trouble with Hank; he never seemed to own up to his mistakes the way most men did. Instead, he'd go off and find a corner to brood in.

"You get old as I am, son — hell, as old as I *feel* — you'll know I'm right." I set down the plate and poured myself more coffee, hesitating only for a moment before pouring an extra cup and handing it to the kid. I reckon it was my own way of making him feel welcome without committing myself to anything. "If a man's smart, he'll make a few decisions early in life about what it is he's going after. Only one problem with that, though."

"What's that, Mister Hooker?" I had the boy's attention all right, for he was hanging on every word I spoke. Pa once said that when young 'uns start acting that way, why, it's a sure sign you're getting as old as you look. And I don't mind telling you that if you aren't in the right frame of mind when it happens, it tends to hurt near as much as a bullet wound.

"Mother and Father," I said with a smile.

"Mother and Father?"

"Sure. Mother Nature and Father Time."

He gave a slight chuckle at the humor in what I'd said, but I was dead serious about it.

"If it ain't Mother Nature, it's Father Time that takes a hand in rearranging your line of thought. Pa said it was what keeps life interesting," I told him.

"Gee, I never thought of it that way."

"You got a name?"

"Colorado Johnny."

"You pin that on yourself, or did someone else do it for you?" I knew it wasn't his real name, but a man could and did pick and choose just about any kind of monicker he wanted in this land, especially if John Law was after him three counties back.

"A little of both, I reckon." He shrugged in a shy manner. "I been pretty much on my own since I was ten or twelve, it seems." His story wasn't all that unusual, for there were a whole lot of kids out here who had the same kind of background. Youngsters who'd been the only survivors of a renegade Indian raid because their folks hid them in the root cellar before they got killed. Kids who'd grown up fast and hard, doing everything from swamping a saloon to pitching hay for a meal and a place to lay their head for the night. If they were lucky, they'd find someone who'd treat them right and show them respect and what it was to give respect in return. If they were lucky. The ones who never came across that sort of luck . . . well, they were the ones who turned out like Carver. Colorado Johnny, or whatever his name was, had been one of the fortunate ones.

"You know, Mister Hooker, you remind me of Mister Odom." It was the first time I'd been compared to someone in a favorable way in some time.

"Oh? And how's that?" I asked.

"He was a kindly old man I knew oncet," Johnny said in that shy way he had about him, that had replaced the mask of toughness he'd worn before. "Oh, not that you're old, Mister Hooker," he added apologetically when he saw the look on my face, "but Mister Odom, I reckon he'd seen a good bit of the world, too, for he sure was full of knowledge and all." He was looking into the empty coffee cup, seeing the past before his eyes. And it was kind of strange, because the smile on his face said he was remembering the good times with Mister Odom, but the look in his eyes told me it was a bittersweet memory. Somehow I knew that Mister Odom hadn't made it; the old man wasn't speaking all of that knowledge any more.

"Taught me to read and write, he did," Johnny said.

"Them are the best kind, Johnny." I filled our cups one last time, drinking the contents in silence. I found myself wondering why Hard Luck Hank couldn't be more like the youngster seated next to me. It wasn't that Hank was a bad character, you understand; it was just that he hadn't fully grown up yet. Oh, he was man-size and all, but the man in him was still acting like a boy who don't want to let go of the fun he's been having as a child. I reckon that was why Hank enjoyed getting other people in trouble so much, mostly at their expense. I also knew that I probably wasn't the only one who'd been around Hank who'd asked himself when he was going to grow up. I was thinking that what Hank needed was a dose of his own medicine, when Colorado Johnny spoke up.

"Why do they call you Guns?" It was an honest enough question, so I spent a few minutes telling him. Fact is, I was beginning to wonder if he'd been curious around Mister Odom, or if Mister Odom had been full of patience, which I wasn't.

"Mister Hooker?" he asked when I was done.

"Johnny, why don't you call me Guns . . . or Matt. Take your pick. Hell, everyone else does." That pleased him, being accepted like that. "Now, what is it, son?"

"Well, do you really think that was true, what you said about a body's line of thought changing?"

"Seems to me I did a fair job of changing your mind the last run-in I had with Carver."

"Yeah," he said, turning a shade red for not remembering what should have stuck in his mind, "I reckon you did."

"Well, there you go." I gave him a quick smile, took my last sip of cold coffee, and was tossing the remains when I saw Hard Luck Hank across the camp and an idea came to me. "Fact is, Johnny, I'm gonna give you a real-life demonstration." I was talking to Johnny, but it was Hank I had my eye on as a smile came to my face. "Yes, sir, boy, right this very night."

I had the idea pretty much in mind by then, even letting Colorado Johnny in on some of it. The sun was about down, and I figured it would take all of an hour to set everything in motion.

Johnny spent the better part of that hour jawing with Hank while I got Bat Masterson and a handful of the boys and told them what I had in mind. One thing about people like Hank was that they liked to talk a lot about what they were going to do in some adventuresome moment in their lives, but the truth was most of them were flat-out pilgrims who couldn't wade through a stream without drowning, let alone walk on water. The trouble with people like that is they sometimes turn into braggarts, and I'll guarantee you there ain't nobody in this land that has any use for a flannelmouth. In the case of Hard Luck Hank, as I've said, he'd let it be known that he had a real itch to see if he couldn't shoot up the whole Comanche nation.

"Say, Hank," Bat said, as he and I approached the would-be skinner and Johnny, "how'd you like to do some turkey hunting with Guns and me?"

"Turkey hunting?" As I'd expected, he was bewildered at best. "But fellas, it's dark."

"Oh, that's no problem," Bat assured Hank. "After sunset's when they settle down. Makes it easier to catch 'em off-guard. Besides, there's a moon out, so they won't be hard to spot." I didn't know what kind of a line Bat was feeding Hank, but it wasn't all a lie. After all, there was a moon out, and we'd all seen what must have been at least a hundred turkeys in the area, especially above camp near the grove of cottonwoods.

"Really? I've never done that before."

"He's right, Hank," Johnny said with a straight face. "We used to do that all the time back home."

So Hank, Bat, and I got our rifles and headed toward that cottonwood grove in search of turkeys. We were halfway there when Bat held out an arm in front of Hank and we stopped.

"Better be careful, Hank," he said in a whisper. "See that fire over there?"

"Yeah, why?"

"I'd bet money it's a Comanch' camp."

"Really?" There was a curious mixture of fear and hope in Hank's face now. "How can you tell?"

"Why, the way they make the campfire, of course." Then, glancing past Hank to me, Bat said, "What do you think, Guns?"

"Definitely Comanch', Bat. And they're some of the meanest."

"Really?" Hank wasn't missing a word, and by the look of him, he was by now having serious reservations about whether he should have come along or not.

Suddenly two shots rang out, clipping branches off two trees we stood by, and all three of us fell to the ground. Bat and I pulled out our six-guns, but Hank couldn't move. He just kept staring out into the darkness, his eyes so big you'd think they would fall out any second.

"Run for it, Hank!" Bat yelled as a second volley of shots rang out. "Guns and me'll hold 'em off."

"Yeah," I said, "you get the boys back at camp!"

Bat and I started firing out above the trees while Hank, not waiting for a second invitation, jumped up and ran like hell. We fired a couple more shots above the trees before looking back to see Hank still running. Bat and I stood up and waved our arms as Charlie Myers and three others emerged from the trees, firing offhand shots into the air occasionally. They would fire until their guns were empty and then come into camp.

Bat and I hightailed it back to the outskirts of camp in time to see Hard Luck Hank standing near the campfire, talking just as fast and furious as the town gossip.

"They're out there! The Comanche! A whole tribe of 'em! A whole nation of 'em!

Guns and Bat are holding 'em off!" He fell to his knees then, more scared than exhausted, as pale as a ghost.

"And you *left* 'em!" Colorado Johnny said.

"No real man would ever do that," another man said, an ornery look on his face.

"But they sent me back!" Hank pleaded, still on his knees. "I didn't run out on 'em! I —"

"Did ya know ya been shot, Hank?" a voice from behind him said as someone poured the remains of the still-hot coffee grounds on his back.

Hank let out a yell, then his face turned as white as Mama's sheets, and it wasn't from the pain of the burn he'd just received from the grounds. You see, that was the moment Bat and I walked up on either side of Hank and he thought he was seeing two ghosts.

"Guns! Bat! You're alive! But you were — And I just got —"

"You ain't gonna die, Hank," Bat said, a crooked smile on his face. "Of course, I ain't ever been scalded with coffee like you just been, but . . ." He shrugged, letting the sentence trail off as Hard Luck Hank began to realize what had happened.

"You mean you ain't shot, and they wasn't Comanches out there and —" The color was coming back to his face now in the form of dark red, and I stepped up to him and grabbed a fistful of his hair, yanking it back so he'd see me eye to eye.

"How's it feel to be on the dirty end of the stick, Hank?" I wasn't smiling when I said it. Bat and some of the others had gotten a laugh at this greenhorn's being made a fool of, but I had more in mind than just that. "Good thing they didn't tear your shirt off and pour it on your bare skin, Hank; you'd be in pain twice as long."

"If that was a joke, I didn't like it," he said angrily, trying to shake his head free of my grip.

"Maybe for some it was, but not for me, Hank. I just wanted you to see how irresponsible you really are and what happens when we have to rely on pilgrims like you in a tight spot. If that was the real McCoy back there, Bat and I would've died for sure, the way you left us."

"He's right, Hank," Johnny said, glancing at me. "I've been in a couple of rough scrapes, and if you got a pard, why, you got to stand beside him, not turn tail and run. It's expected of you."

"You still didn't have no reason to pour them coffee grounds on me like you did!" Hank said, now good and mad.

"You want to blame anyone for that, Hank, you blame me," I said. "After the shenanigans you've pulled at other people's expense, you deserve to feel a bit of pain of your own. Besides, that burn you've got is gonna heal a helluva lot faster than the ribs I damn near got busted in the Long Branch."

"There's one other thing," Charlie Myers said, stepping into the light of the clearing. "Guns warned me about you when I took you on. Now I know you ain't had a chance to prove yourself yet, but son, after tonight I've got a feeling you're nowhere near to being as good a skinner as you claim. In my outfit you ride for the brand or not at all. I've got no use for a fraud. So you think on it some tonight, and if you decide by sunup that you can't pull your weight around here, I'd be obliged if you gather your gear and go bother someone else."

Everything he said was true, and Hard Luck Hank knew it. Like it or not, he had been uncovered for the true person he really was. But like I said, Colorado Johnny had been lucky enough to come on that Mister Odom he spoke of, and what the old man had taught him began to show now.

"Mister Myers," Johnny said, slowly stepping forward.

"Yes, son."

"I done a fair bit of skinning, sir, and . . . uh . . ."

"Speak up, son. You're among friends."

"Well, I was thinking, sir, that mebbe I could teach Hank here the ropes if'n he's willing to pull his share." Johnny shrugged, not sure if he'd said the right thing.

"Lad's right, Charlie." I threw in my vote of confidence. "All of us had to start somewhere. And I was gonna take Colorado John here on as my skinner anyway." That last was a bit of a surprise for the boy, but it showed in his eyes that he was pleased by my decision.

"You willing to take the responsibility for this pilgrim?" Charlie asked Johnny, slowly rubbing his jawline.

"Well, yessir, I reckon I will." He said it without hesitation, like he knew what he was getting into, and that was a good sign . . . for all of us.

"Then there's only one other thing you gotta do, Johnny."

"Yes, sir! You name it!" The boy was eager to please.

"Don't call me sir," the older man said, a smile forming on his face. "Everyone else calls me Charlie, so you might as well, too. Hell, out here you *work* for a living, and ain't no one ever done that got called sir!"

The men laughed, knowing what Charlie meant. And it was about then that a look of hope came to Hard Luck Hank's face as he looked up at his boss.

"Can I call you Charlie too?"

"You, young man," Charlie said in a grim manner, "had better be so busy that I *never* see you again before we get my place built. 'Cause if I do, I'll show you how we make a steer out of a bull!"

The men thought that was funny, too. But most important to me was that I had a new partner for when the season started.

And Hard Luck Hank had done considerable growing up that night.

CHAPTER 6

Charlie Myers never did say just where he wanted his new business located, so we just kept probing deeper south into the Indian Territory. I was scouting the South Canadian when I saw the remains of some buildings and got real cautious approaching them. They looked almighty familiar for some reason, and then it hit me.

What I'd come across was Adobe Walls.

I'd never actually seen it except in my mind, for it was Pa who'd been here with Kit Carson back in '64, and who'd told us boys about how Carson and a couple hundred of his men had stood off nearly a thousand or more Comanche and Kiowa. It wasn't exactly a victory, but it wasn't a defeat either, because they'd let those Plains Indians know who they were tangling with before they got the hell out of there. Pa claimed he nearly had as bad a run-in with a feisty kid named Callahan as he had with the Comanch'; helped this Callahan get his girl back or something like that. Fact is, there was a lawman by that name in one of the Kansas cow towns now, and I briefly wondered if it wasn't the same man.

"There's another good example of Mother Nature and Father Time working hand in hand," I said to Colorado Johnny, who was riding with me that day.

"How's that, Guns?"

"This ain't the Adobe Walls Pa described to me," I said as we rode closer to the structure. "Pa said the walls were ten, twelve, even fifteen feet high in places back then. Shows what ten years can do, I reckon."

At their highest the walls were now only four or five feet in height, a barren shadow of what had been described to me as a legendary battlefield. But then I reckon most legends sort of fall apart as time goes by.

"How much further you think Mister Myers is gonna want to go before he sets up shop?" In his presence, Johnny called Charlie by his first name, but when the man wasn't around, Johnny still talked about him formally.

"If it was me, I wouldn't go no further. Not a-tall," I said.

And Charlie Myers agreed when he saw the Adobe Walls area. It was good buffalo-hunting country, with plenty of water and grazing grass for the horses. Hell, it even had some cottonwoods and a few berry trees if a man took a liking to that sort of fruit. It was a mile or so northeast of the Walls that Charlie decided to make permanent camp. We were right next to running water we called Adobe Creek, and considering the surroundings, that was fine with everyone.

Dirty Face Jones set out with his four-mule wagon to haul logs into camp as we began building what would for the most part be sod houses for the stores. Myers's place was thirty by sixty, and not far away Jim Hanrahan had built himself a similar structure for use as a saloon. Did you ever notice that whenever a new building or store goes up that looks like it'll make a decent go of it, a saloon goes up pretty near to it? It must be a testament to the fact that ever since the beginning of time the only thing man ever wanted more than branch water was a good stiff drink to settle his nerves when he was through with his work. A fellow named O'Keefe built a small blacksmith shop, which brought the number of buildings to three, all log-poled and sod-roofed.

Meanwhile, Billy Dixon and a handful of others had scouted to the south and come across the first buffalo of the season. They furnished us with a combination of buffalo, turkey, and deer meat for meals.

They say in the Good Book that God spent six days making the world and rested on the seventh. Well, us buffalo hunters were building our own little world in that tiny area, but it took more than six days, and I'll guarantee that no one rested until it was done. By the time we were done, we had built an additional store that a newcomer named Rath had taken over to give Myers competition, as well as a storage area and a good-sized corral for our remuda. Someone keeping a diary of sorts had kept track of it all and figured it was around the first of May when everything was open for business.

There's a certain measure of pride a man takes in doing something and doing it well, and I reckon it showed when we all sat down that final day and had a well-deserved drink.

"Tain't nothing fancy like back East, but I reckon it'll do," Johnny said with a smile.

"It's a good thing to keep in mind, Johnny," I said. "People working together is how this land'll be settled. Not by one-man heroes like them dime novels that Hank carries around make out."

"Sounds like it gets hard being your own man sometimes if that's how things have to be."

"It's only as hard as you make it, son."

We sat there in silence for some time before Colorado Johnny decided to get curious about me again.

"Did you ever have a family?"

"Just my Pa and my brother, Diah," I said.

"Never got married or nothing?"

I smiled to myself, thinking back some. "Nope. Confirmed bachelor, I reckon." The lad was curious enough, but he'd learned that prying too much into a man's past can get you in trouble, so he waited for me to volunteer the reason for my smile. "You recall that piece in the Good Book about the Maker spending six days making and resting on the seventh?"

"Sure. I reckon everyone's read that."

"Well, my pa had his own version of that. He claimed that God spent six days creating the earth." I smiled again.

"And he don't believe He rested on the seventh day?" It must have been the boy's first encounter with a contradiction of the Bible for he looked awful serious.

"No. Pa claimed on the seventh day, the

Maker created women . . . and the world ain't been the same since."

He laughed but then turned serious again as he said, "You're joshing me, right?"

"I don't know, son. I never have been much good with women." I shrugged. "So maybe he's right." That was one reason I hadn't gotten hitched so far, and it was as good as any.

We finished the last of our tinful of liquor and rinsed out the cups in the creek. Johnny looked over his shoulder at our creation, studying it a moment.

"What do you think they'll call it?"

"Well, I was talking to some of the boys the other day about that. I don't think there's a lick of adobe in any of what we put up, but I reckon what they chose is as good as anything."

"What's that?"

"Adobe Walls."

CHAPTER 7

Those sod-and-picket buildings that we called Adobe Walls soon became the head-quarters for all of the buffalo hunters in the panhandle area, and the stores and saloon and blacksmith shop did a thriving business from the start. It turned out to be just like Charlie Myers had figured, an area that served as a modern-day rendezvous for buffalo men needing supplies and ammunition. It was also the storage area for the hunters as they brought in wagonloads of buffalo hides. Trouble was it was May already, and the big herds hadn't showed up yet. According to the old-timers, it was because of a late spring, which was as accurate an assessment as any. Still, all a body could do was sit and wait.

It was the end of the second week of waiting that Charlie Myers decided it was time to restock his inventory and asked me to drive the hundred and fifty miles back to

Dodge for supplies. I thought about it for all of a minute before agreeing to the trip, knowing that even if the herds showed up the day after I left, I'd be back within ten days, two weeks at the most, and still be able to get my share of hunting in. Besides, it would give me something to do if it was another two weeks before those hairy beasts made their appearance.

"You gonna take that Colorado boy with you, Guns?" Charlie asked after I'd said I'd go. He sounded a bit apprehensive.

"Johnny? Sure, why?"

"You wouldn't consider doing me a favor, would you?" He said it with the skittishness of an old woman who isn't sure the gossip she's spreading is the truth.

"Favor?"

"I want you to take Hank with you, too," he said quickly, spitting it out so fast I could hardly hear it.

"You ain't serious, Charlie, are you?" It was suddenly apparent what Charlie's favor was going to be.

"Well, dammit, he makes me nervous," he said, a bit of anger showing in him now. "Besides, that boy you got said he'd be responsible for Hank . . . and I'd just as soon not have him around camp."

"Why, you starting to believe his nickname

fits him?" I asked with a smile.

"Well, it does, by Jove! Do you know Harley's rig busted on him a couple days back and Hard Luck Hank wasn't standing no more'n ten feet from him! And Hanrahan's saloon! Why, Jim said they was two bottles of his home brew missing after Hank walked by one afternoon and —"

"All right, Charlie," I said, holding up a hand to fend off any more complaints. "I'll take him off your hands for a week or two." I still hadn't convinced myself that the kid was really a jinx. And as for the whiskey, it was likely that Hank had swiped the bottles.

So we left the next morning, Johnny, Hank, and me, and made the best time we could getting back to Dodge with those empty wagons. And we had not one mishap the whole trip.

I figured one day, two at the most, to load up and get back on the trail to Adobe Walls, but there was quite a bit of to-do when word got around we were back in Dodge. It wasn't half an hour before Sis came running around the corner flying into my arms like some long-lost lover.

"Oh, Matt, I knew you'd come back for me!" she said after she came up for air and let go of me, all of which brought leers from Johnny and Hank.

"I thought you said you wasn't the marrying kind, Guns," Colorado Johnny said.

"Well, I am," I replied, feeling the red crawl up my back and fill out my cheeks. "I mean, I ain't!"

"Oh, don't be silly," Sis threw in. "Matthew is my *true*-love." Then she was kissing me again, but I pulled her loose and held her at arm's length.

"Now, you listen to me, woman. These two lads and I have got work to do, so you git. . . . Go on, skedaddle." I reckon because I wasn't denying what she'd said, she figured that everything was all right between us, and she got that moon-eyed look about her again. All I seemed to be dealing in these days was young kids who took to worshiping me for the wrong reasons.

"Anything you say, Matt," she purred as she left.

"Has she started tucking in your shirttail yet, Guns?" Maybe Hard Luck Hank thought that was funny, but I didn't and poked a long, hard finger into his chest.

"Don't push it, Hank. Remember, you ain't off the hook yet."

"Off the hook?"

"I can find some more coffee grounds to pour down your back if need be."

"All right, all right! I was just funning

you," Hank said, and went back to work caring for the teams.

"I don't know what you're mad about, Guns," Johnny said. "Why, she looks like a right beautiful girl to me."

"Sure, kid, sure," I mumbled. "Now, let's get some work done."

We spent the rest of the afternoon taking care of the animals and then of ourselves before calling it a day. Yet in the back of my mind was the worry of how bothersome Sis was going to be when it came time to get the loading done. After I'd checked on just how much we'd have to take back in the way of supplies and was able to find a couple of young lads who were willing to work for a quarter a day helping with the loading, I pretty well had it figured out.

Yes, sir, I'd figured out a way to get my job done and not have to worry about Sis bothering me for the next day or so.

"Sis, this is Colorado Johnny," I said, introducing the two the next morning. I don't think either one of them was expecting it, but Sis started giving Johnny the eye while the lad got tanglefoot of the tongue and kept turning his hat in hand, as a young man will do the first time he comes across a good-looking girl.

"Pleased to meet you," she said, offering her hand. Like I said, she was eyeing Johnny, and that was fine with me. I knew I'd hurt her by flat-out rejecting her, but she was young enough to find a new beau, and the way she was looking at Colorado Johnny, I had a hunch he was it.

Johnny, well, I'd say he hadn't done much courting in his day. He took her hand the same as any man he'd ever met and gave it a good pump just to prime the well before muttering, "Yes, ma'am, pleased to meet you, too."

"Guns, what are you doing?" Hank asked, setting down a sack of flour.

"Get back to work, Hank." I said it out of the side of my mouth and as low as I could, knowing that if there was one thing Hard Luck Hank could do well, it was spoil what a body had planned.

"This is Johnny's first time in Dodge, Sis. I thought you might be able to show him around. He's already said he thought you're a mighty pretty lady, and I figure you know the town as well as anyone." Not that Dodge was all that much to look at, but a couple of young kids like these weren't liable to need much of an excuse to be in each other's company. What I was gambling on was that the girl wouldn't recognize the boy as hav-

83

ing been a one-time partner of Carver now that Johnny had a clean shave, a haircut, and some decent clothes.

"But Guns, what about the supplies? And I ain't got any money; you know that. Why I couldn't take this young lady —"

"You've got an advance on your pay now," I said, digging into my pocket and forking over a mixture of coin and paper to Johnny. "As for the supplies, why, Hank said he'd be able to pull your share of the loading without a problem at all." I gave a condescending look to the man at my side. "Ain't that right, Hank?"

"Yup. That it is, Guns," he replied through grit teeth, glancing first at the boy, then at me. "I just can't wait to see if I can't break my back loading these supplies."

"Well, I don't know what to say." Johnny was sort of mystified about the whole thing, but I just shooed them on, knowing that Sis would say everything for him before he even got the chance.

"Guns, that ain't fair," Hank said after they'd left, "you letting him go and keeping me here. I could take a real dislike to you for that sort of thing."

"Let's get one thing straight, Hank," I said, planting my hands on my hips as I glared down at the smaller man. "Liking ain't got a damn thing to do with getting a day's work done, so you can hate my guts for all I care as long as you do your job. As for fair, it seems to me you're pretty quick to forget that it was that lad who kept you in a job when the rest of the camp was ready to throw you out. So you see if you can't work up a sweat on more than just your upper lip."

Those three boys I'd hired did more than their share of the loading that day. But then when you're twelve pushing fourteen, I reckon you try hard to prove that you've got it in you to be as much a man as your pa or anyone who takes you on for a job. I was more than pleased with the work that had been done by the end of the day and gave each of them a dollar for their efforts, rather than the agreed-upon two bits, and mentioned that they each now had another dollar's worth of credit toward the candy jar at the general store to boot.

They had gone off, and I was explaining to Hank that the next morning we'd load a couple of extra pack mules before we left, when one of the boys came running back up to me, a mad look on his face.

"He ain't gonna give us none, Mister Hooker!" he blurted out.

"Who? What are you talking about?" I asked.

"The man at the general store. You said we could have some candy, but he says we can't!"

"Oh? Well, we'll get that taken care of right now." I'd been over to the store about noon and had told the owner the boys' names and given him three dollars in advance, explaining my proposition to him, and he'd said there'd be no problem. From the look on this boy's face, I was beginning to wonder if the man didn't like kids or was just being spiteful. "Hank, clean this place up and head over to Fat Jack's. I'll buy you a drink and get us something to eat afterward."

The man tending the counter at the store wasn't the owner I'd spoken to; he was instead a middle-aged man who looked like a man who is constantly being lorded over by his wife. Apparently he took it out on the store customers, no matter what their age.

"What is it you want?" he growled in much the same tone I suspicioned he'd greeted the boys with.

"Well, now, to tell you the truth, I'd like what they call service with a smile. But if you're not willing to give me that, I'll settle for a talk with the owner."

"Well, he's not here. Now, what the —" He stopped short, a gleam entering his eye as if everything was clear to him now, like it had come to him in a dream as those fancy writers put it. "Oh, I see. You're here about these brats and their supposed candy."

The three boys were there all right, and none of them was any too happy about being called a brat.

"Now, boys, there's a valuable lesson to be learned here," I said as calmly as possible, although inside I had the urge to kill this loudmouth.

"Sir?" one of them asked, confused.

"Always take care of the men in your outfit." I no sooner had said it than I snaked out my right arm and grabbed the clerk by the throat, my fist nearly encompassing the whole of his neck. I pulled him forward some, as far as he could lean over the counter before his eyes looked like they'd fall out of their sockets. When I spoke, it was in a hard slow voice. "These young lads just got through putting in a man's worth of work today, which is likely more than you've ever done in your entire life. Now, *friend,* if you don't get *real* polite *real* soon I'm gonna snap your neck in two like it was a twig." Of a sudden he was awful quiet.

"Here, here! What's going on?" It was the voice of the owner, the older man I'd spoken to at noon. He'd just come out of the back room.

"You've got lousy help, mister," I said, pushing back the clerk as I released my grip on him.

"He . . . tried to . . . choke me!" The man was barely getting the words out, which was fine with me. But it was the owner I wanted to talk to now.

"As I recall, I made a deal with you about some credit for these lads concerning your candy jar."

"That is correct, sir," the owner acknowledged.

"Then maybe you'd better pass it on to your hired help or start tending the desk yourself. Now, I don't know where you picked up this pilgrim, but every time he opens his mouth, you're losing a customer."

"I don't understand."

I explained to the man what had happened to the boys and how obnoxious the clerk had been when I'd approached the counter.

"No one likes being treated like of pile of manure, mister," I said, "least of all me. So if he's the best you can do for help, I'll take my business elsewhere." The story seemed to shock the man, particularly the part about his clerk's behavior.

"Is that true, Mister Fannish?" he demanded. When the clerk looked away and didn't answer, the owner turned his attention back to me. "Perhaps you're right, sir. Perhaps I should do more of my own clerking.

"As for you three," he said, looking down at the lads, "I'm terribly sorry about the rudeness Mister Fannish showed you. In fact, I'll tell you what. I'll double the amount of the credit your friend here put up for you. But only under one condition."

"Yes, sir! Anything!" The oldest did the talking for them, but all three of them were equally excited.

"Don't eat it all in one day." The older man smiled as the boys made their way to the end of the counter near the door and each took a small fistful of hard candy from the jar. As they did, he motioned for the clerk to come to him. When he spoke, it was me he was talking to, but the clerk was the one who had to withstand his boss's glare.

"As for Mister Fannish, I'm afraid his services in this store have come to an end. He'll be getting his last pay at the end of the day."

I'd become so embroiled in what was going on that I'd plumb dropped my guard.

"He ain't the only one whose services are coming to an end today," a cold, hard familiar voice behind me said. When I turned around, I saw Lance Carver standing in the doorway. He was still piss-ugly mean, still looking, acting, and sounding like he was ready to kill anyone who got in his way. And the look in his eyes said that I had just gotten in his way — or at least he'd put me there.

"Sir, there'll be no gunplay in my establishment." As firm as the older man tried to sound, I could tell it was a hollow threat. He, like many a city dweller, had come across the Lance Carvers of the world before and knew that they could be deadly no matter what was said to them, especially to those who said it.

"He's right, Carver," I said. "You got something you want to settle with me, I'll be more than willing to meet you at the city limits." It wasn't the general store being shot up that worried me so much as it was the three youngsters who were now in the line of fire if something did happen. It also crossed my mind that I'd left the Sharps back with Hank and the wagons and only had my Colt's and bowie to defend myself with.

It was when Carver saw me give a quick glance at the kids that he suddenly turned the pistol in his hand on one of the boys at the counter. "Put your gun on the counter, Hooker," he said in that determined way he had. "I'm gonna kill you slow, one bullet at a time." When I hesitated, he stuck the barrel of his pistol in the boy's chest. "You don't, I'll kill him first."

I was just placing my hand on the butt of the Colt's when I heard Colorado Johnny's voice somewhere out in the streets.

"You drop it, Lance, or I'll kill you where you stand." It was Johnny all right, and he sounded as if he meant what he said, but I didn't know if he was aware of the situation here inside the store, and for a moment I feared he'd make the wrong move.

"I got a boy here under the gun, sonny. You —"

He never finished it, for a shot rang out from outside and Carver's pistol went flying from his fist along with a parcel of what must have been flesh and blood. Carver never even got off a shot, for he had been in the process of cocking his gun when Johnny shot it from his hand.

But he was gamey, that Carver; I'll say that for him. Blood and all dripping from his hand, he still reached for the bowie at his side. One way or another he was going to do everything he could to do me in. That's when I pulled out my own Colt's and shot him. I'm better with a long gun than I am with a pistol, so the shot didn't kill him outright. It hit him high and left in the chest, more in the shoulder region than anywhere else, and spun him around. That was when Johnny shot him full in the chest and he fell back inside, dead.

"You all right, son?" I asked as I placed a steady hand on a frame that was visibly shaking from top to bottom.

"He almost —"

"Yeah, I know, son" were the only words I could find as I stared down at the body before us. "Killing ain't nothing you ever get used to." Times like that it's hard for me to find any right words of comfort, so I stick to the truth and hope it doesn't hit too hard.

"What happened here?" were the next words I heard as the marshal pushed his way through the crowd that had gathered about the doorway.

"I killed him," Johnny said, plain and simple.

"Then I think you'd better come with me, son," the lawman said.

"He done it to save my life," I said, thinking maybe we could settle it all right here and now. "Fella had it in mind to kill me and decided to take one of these youngsters with me as well."

"That's right, marshal," the store owner said, and proceeded to explain in detail what had happened. He must have been one of the more-respected men in town, for the marshal called it self-defense then and there. But he must have had it figured that if I hadn't been around to cause the trouble in the first place, it never would have happened.

"I don't like killing in my town, mister," he said to me.

"Well, marshal, I'm not too keen on it my own self, especially when I'm the one someone's trying to make dead meat out of. But don't you worry none. Me and my crew will be leaving tomorrow, once we're finished with our business."

"Good," the lawman said, "I'll be glad to see you go."

Sometimes it just doesn't pay to go bucking the tiger with the local law, no matter what you think of them, so I let it all end right there with the marshal feeling like he'd done something important.

"I'll bet you will, marshal. I'll bet you will."

CHAPTER 8

I spent a good share of that night trying to forget about Lance Carver and the killing and ignoring the strange looks I got in Fat Jack's saloon. I reckon people get citified and all of a sudden they're respectable; more so than the rest of us because they're around more folks they have to impress. So they start giving you looks like you're some kind of ogre that ain't fit to inhabit their town. Me, I never took to killing unless I'd been prodded into it and figured no other man would have done any different. As for impressing anyone, well, hitting them square between the eyes with a good hefty piece of deadwood is as good as anything for that; Pa always said it worked fine on jackasses, and I was beginning to think this town was inhabited by more and more of them.

I didn't even think about Colorado Johnny until the next morning after I'd gotten up. I remembered he'd been with Sis when he'd shot Carver and had seemed to fade into the background after the marshal had left. But what was even more of a surprise was the fact that Sis hadn't come forward and gone into some dramatic act about how I'd almost been killed, like she had a way of doing. Hell, maybe she had taken a real liking to Johnny and that had gotten me off the hook as far as being some kind of love interest for her.

"I owe you one, Johnny," I said when the lad approached the wagons and I offered my hand. He took it, and I slapped him on the shoulder with my other hand. Times like that I near forget my own strength, because he almost fell over sideways. "Too bad you didn't stick around last night. I'd have bought you a drink," I said.

"Well, Cissy was there, and like you told her to, she was showing me around the town, so —"

"Sure, I understand." I smiled and poured him a cup of the coffee that had just come to a boil.

"What are you doing building a fire here at the edge of town?" he asked after taking the cup. "There's a bakery down the street that opened a couple hours back that'll serve you coffee. Seems to me this is just a waste of our supplies."

So I told him about how some of the looks I'd received the night before could likely have killed just as bad as that bullet he'd put in Carver if they were lead. But the whole idea seemed to confuse Johnny.

"Why you?" he asked, pouring more coffee as Hard Luck Hank began to stir in his blankets. "I thought I was the one who done him in."

"Oh, you did, kid, and I'm grateful to you for it. You saved my bacon. It's just that I've got a bit of a reputation in these parts for drawing trouble. Happens damn near every spring when we get together to wait for the herds to come north." I paused a moment as I looked at Johnny over the rim of my cup. "That was some mighty fancy shooting you done yesterday. Knowing you could shoot that good might make a body cautious." I took another sip of coffee. "You must have practiced a long time to get that good."

Not many men ever got real nosy about another man's past out here. You might say it was an unwritten law of the land. There were enough lawmen and Pinkertons trying to track down men who'd had a bad run of luck and decided it was their time to do some taking now and had lifted a few dollars to make up for it. Enough to make a man who'd run afoul of the law in the next territory get real cautious about what he said and who he said it to. But I'd obliged Colorado Johnny and told him bits and pieces about my own past as he'd inquired about it, so I figured it was his turn to do a bit of explaining now.

"Yeah, I've practiced," he said, his face tightening up, the voice taking on a serious tone, "eight, maybe ten years. I never did count exactly.

"You asked me about my name once, Guns, about whether I'd hung it on myself or whether someone else had. Well, I reckon I picked it. You see, there was this fella back before the war by the name of Eldorado Johnny who thought he was good with a gun. And I reckon he was, at least from the stories I heard. But he went up against another gunman named Langford Peel at Virginia City during the silver strike days and got hisself killed." He paused, smiling briefly, remembering the past. "Mister Odom never thought much of the likes of Eldorado Johnny."

"The way you were talking about Mister Odom, I didn't figure he'd be the type," I said.

"I reckon when you're a kid and you find someone who's got the same name you do

. . . well, you figure you're just bound to grow up to be like 'em, especially if you admire 'em." It struck me then that the lad before me wasn't really a lad at all but a full-grown man with a boyish face. He might be twenty years old, but he'd aged into manhood sometime back. I could see it in his face as he continued his story.

"One day two men showed up. One of them was a smooth talker; the other one was tall with a jagged scar on his face. Mister Odom didn't do much shooting lessen it was to put food on the table. God, he was a gentle man," Johnny said, only this time his face was filled with pain and regret. "I wasn't much more'n twelve, I don't think. That smooth talker, he was a gambler down on his luck, and the other man, well, he turned out to be flat-out mean. Mister Odom, he said there was two kinds of people in the world, givers and takers. Those two men, they were takers. They beat Mister Odom within an inch of his life, and then they killed him and took what they wanted. I tried to stop 'em, but the plug ugly cut me." Johnny undid the first few buttons of his shirt and pulled back the left side, revealing a fading scar that ran from the top of his shoulder about six inches down toward the center of his chest.

"You didn't have to show me that, son," I said. "I believe you." You get so you can pretty much tell when a person is putting you on and when he's telling the truth, and from what this boy was reliving from his past, I'd have had a hard time believing he was making it up.

"Yeah, Guns, I practiced," he continued. "I practiced a lot. I buried Mister Odom and spent a month getting my strength back and taking care of the animals he had. I found an old Navy cap 'n' ball pistol he had hid away, and I practiced with it. Fast didn't come until later. I spent that month getting good with that gun. When I left, I turned the animals loose — ain't no one should be penned up. I traded his books for supplies and ammunition." Johnny had a grim look about him when he looked at me. "Yeah, Guns, I practiced a lot." He tossed the cold coffee out and handed the cup to me. "I got to get rid of some of this coffee."

"Johnny," I said as he turned to go, remembering that he hadn't been around the day before and didn't know what I had planned for today. But he must have thought I was still dogging him about his story, because he stopped and glanced over his shoulder.

"For the book, Carver was the third man

I've killed. The other two —" He paused and shrugged. "Well, one of them was dressed like a gambler and the other had a jagged scar on his face."

"Get up, Hank," I said, kicking the sleeper's blankets as I watched Johnny walk off. "We got work to do."

We were all sort of quiet that morning as we loaded those pack mules. There was either a bit of tension in the air or a silent agreement between us that it was a time for work rather than anything else, because we had those mules loaded in what must have been a record time.

Then Sis showed up, dressed in pants and a man's shirt that was half-hidden by a beaded buckskin jacket. She even sported a brand-new hat.

"A little out of costume, aren't you, Sis?" I said with a smile.

It threw me when she smiled back and said, "Of course not," but then you never can tell about women.

"You sure you ain't been reading those dime novels again?" I asked.

"You mean you didn't tell him?" she said to Colorado Johnny, who was by now turning just a shade darker than the tan on his face.

"Well . . . no, not exactly."

"*Tell* me?" I asked. "You'll pardon me all to hell and gone if I'm mistaken, children, but I thought *I* was in charge of this outfit." Cocking a curious eye toward Johnny, I said again, "*Tell* me?" There I was standing in front of three youngsters, any two of which couldn't total my age combined; for an instant I wondered if those three boys I'd had working with me yesterday might not have been a better bet than the three before me now. At least the boys had been willing to learn. Hell, all these three had done at one time or another was give me orders.

"Cissy's going with us back to Adobe Walls," the lad blurted out.

"Oh? Is that so?" It's not like I threw the question out for discussion, you understand.

"Now, Guns, you hold it right there," Johnny said, holding a hand up as if it would stop me from whatever it looked like I was going to do next. "Hank said you was leaving today, and I've taken a liking to Cissy here and . . . well, dammit, Guns, I saved your life! You said so your own self. Don't you think you owe me that much?" The boy was trying to sound forceful but wound up with a bit of pleading in his voice by the time he was through jawing.

"Look, Johnny, taking her out there might be putting our lives in that much more danger," I said. "Places we're going, she may not even make it out alive herself, and I never carry any dead weight in my outfit."

"Oh, she wouldn't be dead weight, Guns, not at all!"

"That's right, Matt," Sis said, speaking up. "You have to admit I did a pretty good job of patching up your ribs."

"I'm not denying that, Sis. It's just that I don't favor the idea of taking you along for the sole purpose of being a Florence Nightingale to me or anyone else."

"Please, Matt!" She pleaded. "I won't be a problem."

"It's not being a problem I'm thinking about. It's being useful." I gave her a hard look. "Can you tend stock?"

"No."

"Lock and load a pistol and rifle?"

"No."

"Cook?"

"Wel-l-l-l . . ." She drew it out, a look of doubt on her face. "Johnny can teach me! Honest he can, Matt." Suddenly she was there in my arms, her face buried in my chest, hanging on for dear life to the frame of my body. The well was getting ready to overflow when she looked up at me again. "Please, Matt. I promise I won't be a nuisance to you."

I never did find out whether she was using her woman's ways to get what she wanted or if she was really sincere in what she said, but I couldn't stand to see a woman cry, so I gave in.

"All right," I said, holding her at arm's length. "But you get this straight, young lady. *I'm* bossing this outfit, and that means you do as I say, no matter what you think of it."

"Anything you say, Matt."

"As for Johnny here teaching you what you don't know," I said, shifting my gaze to her new boyfriend, "well, he's gonna have all of a week's worth of time to teach it to you. And I'll tell you this, the both of you. If things ain't right by the time we get to the Walls, I'll turn you both over to the hostiles."

"Yes, sir," Johnny said, although I don't know what in hell he was smiling for unless he was just acting the role of a lovesick fool. "You won't be disappointed in Cissy. Why, she'll be a real help to Mrs. Rath when we get to the Walls."

I'd forgotten about the wife of one of the merchants who'd set up shop at Adobe Walls being there and could only pray that having one more of the female species around that many men wasn't going to disrupt things anymore.

"What are you smiling about, Hank?" I said as the flannelmouth of the outfit grinned ear to ear. The last few days he'd had a way of falling back on his old ways and was taking too much pleasure in the misfortunes of others again, basically mine.

"Just thinking, Guns, just thinking," He said it in that mischievous way he had, the one I didn't like.

"You know, Hank," I said, picking up the near-empty coffee pot and pouring the last of the contents into my cup but keeping the pot in my other hand, "Charlie Myers has got it in his mind that you're living up to your name, Hard Luck Hank. And I'll tell you something, Hank. I'm about to be a convert to his way of thinking my own self. You know what else, Hank?"

"What, Guns?" He had a leery look about him, the way a body will look suspiciously out of the corner of an eye at you.

"Things don't work out with these two" — I nodded toward Sis and Johnny, who were now holding hands — "on the way down to Adobe Walls . . . well, I might just figure you put a hex on 'em and blame you for the whole damn thing."

"Oh no, Guns, you wouldn't do that to me," he said in a desperate way.

"Do I have your word you won't cause any trouble?"

"My *word?*" He knew what I meant all right; it's just that Hank likely hadn't ever had to give his word on anything.

I hefted the coffeepot in my hand. "I wonder where'd be a good place to get rid of these grounds."

"You've got it! I'll give you my word! Honest, Guns, I won't be no trouble at all! You won't even know I'm around."

"I'll remember you said that, son."

Then I tossed the remains of the coffee onto the slowly dying fire, and Hard Luck Hank breathed a sigh of relief.

CHAPTER 9

Naturally, I wasn't about to leave Sis and her newfound love interest out there in No Man's Land alone. It's just that sometimes you have to put the fear of God in these youngsters to make believers out of them. We made it to Adobe Walls all right, but as it turned out, Sis didn't need any further encouragement from me to pick up as much useful knowledge about firearms as she could on the way.

"You're heading *that* far south!" said one rider, who was sharing our camp the second night out of Dodge. "There's Injun trouble brewing for sure down there." He went on to tell us of an incident he'd heard of in which a couple of buffalo hunters had been killed by savages to the south of Adobe Walls. None of us had said specifically what it was we were doing heading south, but the following morning the rider let us know he had a low opinion of the inhabitants of

Adobe Walls.

"Them people's plum crazy down there! Only a man what's round the bend would ever think of buffalo hunting with as many heathens on the loose as they is." When he saddled up, he thanked us for our hospitality and the meals and bade us well. "But you stay away from Adobe Walls," he warned. "Them folks is loco."

The stories the man had told got Sis real interested in doing her part to keep us alive and well. They also got me to thinking back on what I should have been remembering all along, that the Plains tribes were back on the warpath.

It had been nearly a year before that Satanta and Big Tree of the Comanche and Kiowa had been released from the custody of the U.S. Army. After raising a good bit of hell in the area, the two Indian chiefs had been captured by the Army and held in a prison of sorts. And by rights that's where they should have stayed, if you were to ask any frontiersman who'd had to tangle with them. Trouble was those brotherly love folks the Quakers decided to get involved with these two particular captives and wound up putting enough pressure on the government to persuade them to let the two chiefs go free, as long as they promised to live peacefully. Ask any one of us out here what we thought of that idea, and you'd likely get only one answer: *HORSE APPLES!* Only you'd get it in a lot more colorful lingo. The result of freeing Satanta and Big Tree was about what you'd expect; or maybe I should just say that if a good many of us ever saw a Quaker on this side of the Mississippi, we could make sure he wanted to spend the rest of his life back in his own part of the world, for they sure weren't wanted in ours.

All during the fall of last year and into the Winter there had been raids by the Comanche and Kiowa in the Texas Panhandle area before they hibernated for the coldest months. There had been a mention here and there as the hunters rode into Dodge that spring about the possibility of more raids starting up, but nothing of a drastic nature had happened so far. That is, not until that rider had told those stories the night before of the fighting down by Adobe Walls. Hearing that kind of news is a reminder to you that you can't let your guard down all that much no matter how much fun you're having; and I knew a lot of hunters who thought of buffalo hunting as more of a sport than any sort of job. Instead, you'd be keeping an eye out for hostiles first and buffalo second, if you wanted to stay alive for another season.

That sort of attitude must have sunk in well in Sis's brain, for you've never seen anyone so helpful or wanting to learn so much as she did the rest of our journey. Unless it was Hard Luck Hank. Until that trip he'd had little interest in weapons of any kind, but after hearing those stories, I found myself spending a good share of my free time breaking down, explaining, and putting together every short and long gun I had for him and Sis.

By the time we made it to Adobe Walls, to my amazement, the two people I'd figured for being the most useless I'd seen in a long time, Hard Luck Hank and Sis, were catching on right quick to how to survive on the frontier.

"Didn't ya get raided by the Comanch' on the way down!?" one hunter asked as we pulled in, rushing up to our wagons.

"Nope," I said, obviously disappointing him, from the change of expression his face took on. "But I heard you lads have had a bit of a scare down here." I glanced over at Charlie Myers as I dismounted from the wagon. "Any truth to it, Charlie?"

"Seems to be," he said, a worried air about him. The anxiety seemed to ease some when he lifted the tarp from my wagon and saw

109

that I'd brought extra ammunition for all our buffalo guns and other firearms.

"Is it that bad?" I asked.

"I'm afraid so, Guns," he said. He gave a quick glance over the cargo before his eyes stopped on Sis and about fell out. "Whoa, now! How could you do it to me, Guns? How could you!!"

"What? Oh, you mean —"

"You not only brought Hank back: you brought a *she!*"

"Hanrahan's still open?"

"Sure, but —"

"Let's have a drink, Charlie. You can tell me your woes, and I'll tell you mine."

It took them a while to start to unload the wagons, but I didn't figure it would be too long before the work was finished, the way Colorado Johnny was lecturing those men about Sis and how he expected them to treat her. In the meantime Charlie and I had a couple of drinks while I told him how I'd gotten roped into letting Sis come along and he told me how bad the Indian situation was getting down here. Believe me, his story was a lot worse than mine.

There had been at least three separate incidents since I'd left in which hunters had been killed by raiding Comanches, who had left a total of six men dead so far.

110

"And one of them was almost Billy Dixon," Charlie said. Bat Masterson and Billy Dixon were probably the youngest hunters in the group that spring other than Hank and Johnny. Both Bat and Billy were likable lads whom Charlie had taken under his wing on this expedition, so it was expected that he'd make a big to-do about one of them getting into trouble.

On an excursion to the south, Billy had left the two men he was with and ventured a bit further on his own, coming across a couple of dead Englishmen who'd been killed by the Comanches. It put enough of a scare into him that he'd gathered up his partners and headed back to camp at Adobe Walls. Not that Billy's life had actually been threatened, but that was the way Charlie told the story.

For a while the men had been overly cautious because of the Indian scare and had stayed in camp, drinking and playing cards for the most part. That had lasted for a few days, because the hunting had really been scarce. But then they'd heard it one day, the sound a train will make when it's crossing a bridge far away. Any greenhorn would figure it was some railroad over yonder that was making the noise, but once you've been on the hunt for a season or so, you'll swear you know the sound by heart. The noise, you see, was being made by the massive herds that had finally migrated far enough north. That was when some of the men had gotten their brave up and decided that it was time to hunt buffalo, Indians or no. The smart ones did their hunting to the north, since all of the raids had so far come from the south of camp.

"Billy Dixon's got gumption. I'll say that for him," Charlie said, pouring us another drink. "Good thing you come back when you did, too, Guns. He's spent the better part of the day seeing if he could get a two-week supply together to go back to Moore's Creek where he had his original camp. Ain't many of 'em that care to try that part of the country right now."

"It's the young ones like Dixon who set out where you and I would know better," I said. "Difference between young and old, I reckon."

"Or alive and dead."

"That, too."

While some of the men in camp were unloading my wagons, others were loading Billy Dixon's for the trip he planned to start the following morning. If anyone was unsure as to the sanity of such a venture, they didn't say so, but I was certain that many of the older men held the same view of it that I did, that the whole idea was reckless to say the least.

I suppose I should have seen it coming, but there's just so much that a body can pay attention to at one time. We had buffalo steaks that night, the first decent meal I'd had since leaving Dodge, and it was then I saw Hard Luck Hank cast an eye toward Sis. Since Colorado Johnny had made it clear to everyone in camp that afternoon that he wouldn't tolerate anyone making advances toward his woman, my feelings had eased some about bringing her to Adobe Walls. Hell, no one had challenged him, so why should there be a problem, right?

But there was.

The problem turned out to be Hank who, for one reason or another, hadn't paid much attention to Johnny's spiel that afternoon. At least that's what it looked like when he walked up to the couple after supper that night.

"Miss Cissy," he said in the politest manner I'd ever seen him use, "I'd admire to take you for a walk tonight."

"A walk?" Johnny sounded as astounded by Hank's request as any of us others who heard it. "Hank, you been working too hard." Perched on a log with Sis, Johnny looked up at the thin man before him and shrugged. "There ain't no place in or around this camp that anyone could walk in privacy. And outside the camp sure ain't safe."

"He's right, Hank," Sis said softly. "Johnny and I were just talking. Besides, I'm not interested in anyone else."

"You mean you wouldn't even talk to me?" Hard Luck Hank had barely looked at Sis up till then, having shown her nearly as little attention as I did but for a different reason. Hank hadn't known she existed, where as I had. Yet from the broken-hearted look on his face now, you'd have thought he'd been in love with her from the first time he'd laid eyes on her. Maybe he was just trying to give Colorado Johnny some competition. I didn't know. What I did know was that I didn't need anyone breaking up camp over some love-struck woman. So I headed for the threesome in a few quick strides to make sure nothing out of the ordinary happened.

"Hank, why don't you come talk to me," I said, gently taking him by the elbow and steering him away. He went reluctantly, but I had a hunch it was the smile on Colorado Johnny's face watching him leave more than me forcing him to go that stirred him up.

"Why did you do that?" he asked in a huff when we were off by the corral.

"No, Hank," I said, "that's my question. Why did *you* do that?"

"Well . . ."

"You're not gonna tell me you're in love with her, are you?" I threw a knowing glance at him just to let him see that if he was indeed about to feed me a line, I wouldn't believe it.

"She's too good for him, Guns." The young man sounded purely frustrated. "She's just too good! Hell, I like her . . . a lot."

"Could be, Hank, but Johnny's in love with her. There's a difference, you know."

"Oh, how would you know?" he said, apparently discounting my every word. "All you talk about is staying unmarried, so how'd you ever come to know about it?"

"True," I admitted. "But I never said I'd never been loved. You chew on that, Hank. You might find that one of the reasons I'm not married is the love I had for a woman once. In fact, Hank, if you did a little more thinking before you spoke and maybe tried looking out for some of the other folks you meet in this land instead of just yourself . . .

well, you might not be known as Hard Luck Hank."

"I don't see how you figure that, Guns."

I shrugged. "You believe what you like, Hank. Me, I always had it in mind that people make their own luck."

"You really think so?" He squinted as though he wasn't sure if I were pulling his leg or not.

"Sure do." I paused. "Look, Hank, you just leave those kids alone and —"

"But she's too good for him, I tell you!"

"That may be, Hank," I said, planting a hard finger in his chest, "but I'm sure the two of them can find that out without your help or mine. So leave 'em alone." I gave an extra push when I said the last, and it didn't set favorably with him.

"Yes, sir, *Mister Hooker.*"

It was still the voice of a frustrated young man talking now, but there was anger building in it, too, and I had a notion that any friendship I'd had with Hard Luck Hank was coming to an end as he walked away.

It was an hour or less to daybreak when I was awakened by voices of two men arguing nearby. Waking up to someone else's problems never did much to improve my mood, so I told myself to figure on one of those days ahead as I threw back the blanket,

116

sloshed on my hat, and felt around for my boots.

"I'm warning you, Hank. You stay away from Cissy. She's my girl. You understand?"

Johnny and Hank were out front next to the overhang of Charlie Myers's store, arguing, as you might expect, over Sis. I could just barely see what was going on, but as soon as I neared the two, I could smell the whiskey on Hank's breath.

"Does either of you know what time it is?" I asked.

But neither of them seemed to care about what I had to say, for it was then that Hank swung out and knocked Colorado Johnny to the ground. Hank appeared quite proud of the feat, from the drunken grin on his face. Johnny on the other hand, didn't think it was so comical at all. His hand went to the butt of his Colt's.

"Hold it!" I said to Johnny loud enough for a good share of the camp to hear in case they were listening. "That's not how you do it, son. Now, you just cool off and get you some air over there," I said, pointing to a wagon some feet off.

"Still doing his fighting for him, *Mister* Hooker?" Hank slurred. He looked like he was as mad at me as he had been at Johnny and figured to do to me what he had done to his first opponent.

"John Barleycorn sure can give a man a case of confidence," I said.

It was a full roundhouse punch he threw at me, just like the one that had knocked Johnny down. But it was slow, and I blocked it with my left arm before bringing the fist down on the side of Hank's face. It staggered him while I brought my own roundhouse right to meet the other side of his face. The blow was hard enough to knock him unconscious, and he fell to the ground. But before he did, he crashed into a supporting pole, and one side of the store's overhang collapsed on top of him.

"That's how you do it," I said to Johnny, rubbing my fist.

"What the hell's going on out here?" more than one man said in a sleepy voice as the camp came to life. "Can't a man get a decent night's sleep?" another threw in.

I was still staring down at the body of Hard Luck Hank, when Johnny spoke up.

"I hope you fellas are wide-awake now," he said to the camp in general.

"Huh?" I asked.

"We got company."

That got everyone's attention right away, but I was the first one to see what he was talking about, while the others were still rubbing their eyes. And damned if the boy wasn't right.

We had visitors all right, and they filled the horizon from one end to the other as the sun broke through. Yeah, *visitors.*

"Jesus, Mary, and Joseph!" I heard one man say in astonishment. "That must be the whole goddamn Comanche nation!"

CHAPTER 10

They were everywhere! Blending in along the tree line in the distance, on the horizon to the east, everywhere. The horses were wearing as much war paint as the warriors riding them. There was a lot of blood-red coloring on them, but that wasn't what was bothering us in the camp right then — it was the sheer massive numbers of Indian braves out there and the horrid fact that we might be decorated in *our own* blood soon. It wasn't long before everyone in camp was up, all thirty of us, including the two women, armed and ready to fight.

The camp we were calling Adobe Walls could hardly be considered a fort, or anything else close to the structure Kit Carson and his men had fought at here a decade ago. Yet I had an eerie feeling that we were about to relive the same ordeal Carson had gone through — with a few variations.

First, we weren't any two or three hundred

volunteers who'd come looking for a fight to begin with. And we clearly weren't on what you'd call the offensive in one of those fancy West Point strategy classes. We were twenty-eight men and two women who were outnumbered forty or fifty to one, the only thing going for us being a goodly supply of ammunition and the weaponry that used it — the Sharps Big Fifty that most of us carried. Those who didn't have the Big Fifty were packing the Sharps in at least a .44 caliber, like the new one Billy Dixon had.

The second big difference between this fight and the previous one was the fact that Carson's men were the hunters, and I don't give a damn what kind of a beast you're talking about, being the hunter is one element that *always* gives you an edge. Along with that, you have to take into consideration that whereas Carson was fighting the Comanches and Kiowas, we were in for a bit more trouble. It wasn't confirmed until some time later, but in that predawn light I thought for sure I spotted not only Comanche and Kiowa warriors but a bunch of Cheyenne to boot. And that meant it was going to be one hell of a fight, because those Cheyenne wouldn't normally even have anything to do with the Comanche or Kiowa, though they were cousins of a sort.

You see, hoss, it wasn't the whole Comanche nation that was getting ready to do battle with us out there; it was the Comanche nation *and then some!*

It was either having some sense knocked into him or the sight of all those Indians that sobered Hard Luck Hank up real quick. The jug of booze in his hand was soon forgotten as he disappeared and exchanged it for his own rifle and pistol.

"Doesn't look like you'll have to worry 'bout hunting any Comanches, Hank," I said, trying to smile in what could be described only as a grim situation. "They've come to you."

"But Guns, they've got us surrounded!" No matter how much he rubbed or blinked his eyes, Hank couldn't believe that there were probably close to a thousand hostiles out in front of him.

"Look on the bright side, Hank," Johnny said. "At least they can't get away."

"But that means . . . we're gonna die." His sudden realization of the fix we were in brought out the panic in Hank, and he started to bolt. The only reason he didn't get far was because I planted a firm hand on his shoulder.

"No it doesn't, Hank. You ain't gonna die as long as you do your job." I glanced at the warriors lined up before us, then back at the two young men next to me. "There's only one thing left for us to do, and that's show 'em."

"Yes, sir," Johnny said without hesitation.

"Show 'em?" It was Hank who was confused.

"Show 'em how to die, Hank," I said, checking my loads. "Show 'em how to die."

While the rest of us were gathering up boxes and ammunition and fixing up as much of a barricade as we could, Billy Dixon ran out near the wagon he'd loaded and grabbed hold of the reins of his horse. Maybe he thought those young bucks had come to steal our remuda, but if he did, he found out otherwise right quick.

One hell of a war whoop went up, and all of a sudden those warriors weren't sitting peacefully on the horizon. It was a head-on assault they were making, and you can bet your ass and anything else you value that those birds had no interest in our mounts at all. No, sir! Those fellas were riding hard, and they were after our scalps!!

Dixon got his horse tied to his wagon, grabbed up his Sharps, and ran for the nearest building, Hanrahan's saloon, stopping only once to think about getting a shot in before coming to the conclusion that it might be unhealthful just then. He had to pound on the door and wait for someone to open it up, but he made it to safety before a barrage of arrows and bullets pounded the storefront.

If there was such a thing as being barbaric, those Indians knew how to go about it. Most of them were at least half-naked, with nothing but a medicine bag around their throats to protect them from evil spirits — or so they believed. From the heavy gunfire that was coming at us, I made a mental note to kill the next Comanchero I came across, because that was about the only way any Indian these days came across a white man's firepower. The Comancheros lived on the fringes of Comanche territory and were well know for trading goods they had killed for and stolen themselves, with the hostiles, especially weapons. If the Comanchero had ammunition for the guns, so much the better, the Comanche thought. And even if the Indians weren't all that accurate with those weapons, they sure did shoot often enough to put a scare in a man. But I had some ideas on that subject my own self.

The chiefs and bravest warriors were right out front where you'd expect them to be, showing how invincible they were so the rest of the tribe would follow. They carried rifles, lances, and shields, some of which were made of hardened buffalo hides. Now, friend, as much as I was getting skittish about being shot at, I figured it was time the other fellows felt the same way. Indians, they put a lot of stock in greater spirits protecting them in battle, but I knew different. So I brought a bead on one of those braves in the front that had a fancy decorated shield and dusted him with my Sharps. Hank and Johnny must have gotten the same idea, for I soon saw them taking aim with their rifles. I don't know if it did any good, but those hostiles tried another tactic after their first couple of passes at us. Instead of a head-on rush, they came riding crisscross right in front of the building, pot-shotting us from the far side of their mounts as they did so. And that put us in a heap of trouble, because the Comanche are about the best horse riders you ever seen in the world.

"Gimme your pistol," I said to Hank as I reached past him and pulled his Colt's from its holster. "Get this loaded for bear, Hank, and stay outta sight." He took my rifle, gladly falling back alongside the building we were next to. "What say we give 'em a dose of their own medicine, Johnny?" I asked.

"You bet." From behind the small of his back, he pulled out a second sixgun and covered me while I ran a dozen or so yards to the Shadler brothers' wagon and rolled partially beneath it. They'd never need the wagon again, for they were dead, as was the dog who'd been their constant companion. Must've gotten killed in their sleep.

Colorado Johnny could handle a pistol like no man I've ever seen before or since that day; I'll give him that. Like I said, those warriors riding back and forth in front of the store were shooting from the undersides of their horses' necks. But with me on one side of them and Johnny on the other as they rode by, well, they were as much sitting ducks as we were.

Slowly the attack became more cautious and the enemy fire was more sporadic, indicating that they hadn't liked the first baptism of fire they'd received from us. The greater mass of hostiles began to withdraw, while some stayed near and hid behind stacks of buffalo hides or the stables. There must have been a few important bodies lying out there, for some of the warriors tried to retrieve them from the field of fire as the battle slowed. One rider came in on a mount and helped up a wounded comrade to the rear of him. By then I had my Sharps in hand again and took aim at the horse, figuring that if I could down him, someone else would get the riders. I shot him high on the left rump, and he faltered for a second, but only for a second, as he raced away, the two riders atop him, a thick trail of blood streaming down his leg. The warriors might live out the day, but I knew that mustang wouldn't.

It was a goddamn waste, killing that mustang, one of the few things in my life that I've ever regretted. If it's possible to experience anger and sorrow at the same time, then I reckon that was how I felt about shooting that horse, but when you're fighting for your life, you do what will keep you breathing, like it or not, and this was one of those times.

Then, for one instant, I had a notion that maybe, just maybe, some humans are touched by the Divine in life. I can't tell you how, but they seem to be protected from harm by their maker, whoever He is in their eyes. I say that because right then one of the chiefs came riding close to camp and drew a hell of a lot of gunfire because of that bonnet he wore. But no one could hit him, and he reached down and picked up a wounded warrior by the arm, pulling him all the way up on to the rear of his own mount without so much as a nick. That's the kind of man who, even if you're his enemy, you have to admire, for what he'd done had taken a lot of guts. But then I guess that's how he'd gotten to wear that fancy bonnet anyway.

"That was Quanah Parker," one of the men said as the three of us took cover inside a store.

"Yeah," I said, almost to myself, "I reckon it had to have been." Then I started reloading my pistols.

The stock fared worse than we did in that first half hour. The oxen and horses of several wagons had been killed, as well as Billy Dixon's mount and a little mustang colt that Mrs. Olds had in camp that was as friendly and tame as any you'd ever seen. Those who'd had it in mind to strike out on a hunt today would find their wagons had been looted by those braves who hadn't been trying their hardest to kill us. By my count, three of our men had been killed, but considering the odds we were up against, that was pretty damn good. For the moment there was a lull in the fighting, and we were all reloading for the next attack.

"Damn!" I heard Bat Masterson say as he looked out the front door of the saloon, the building we were inside.

"What's the matter, hoss?"

"Billy Tyler just took one outside Myers's store." Tyler and Masterson were pretty good friends, which explained Bat's reaction to what he saw.

"Bad, you think?" I said, getting up.

"I don't know, but I'm gonna find out." Bat ducked out the front door of the saloon, heading for Myers's place. Again I handed Hard Luck Hank my Sharps in exchange for his Colt's and ran out the door after Masterson.

Both of us made it to Charlie Meyers's store without much incident, climbing in through a side window. When I got inside, I saw Bat kneeling on the floor, holding his friend's head in his hand, doing his best to comfort him. Trouble is you never can give much comfort to a dying man. If the chest wound he had taken was hurting as badly as it was bleeding, well, he wasn't about to see the sun set that day.

"Water" was all the man could say, but we didn't have any. What the hell, it was a store, not a hotel, so why should there be water? Still, Billy Tyler was pleading for water, and from the look on his face, it was what he wanted most in the world right then.

I don't know what made me do it, no

more than the man in the moon would. Maybe it was seeing Quanah Parker come to the rescue of one of his own men right in our front yard and risk his own life to save that brave. Or maybe it was seeing young Billy Tyler lying there dying and knowing he ought to at least have his last wish. Hell, I knew I wasn't invincible; I knew I could die just as fast and easy as that boy on the floor. But I did it anyway.

"Gimme a bucket," I said. When Bat started to question my sanity, I gave him a hard look and repeated, *"Gimme a bucket,"* but with a bit more force this time.

The nearest water was in the well near the stockade, which was a good ways off. When I had the bucket, I crawled back out the window I'd come in and ran like hell to get to that well. I may be big, but I'm sort of like a train when it comes to running. It takes me a while to get moving real fast, but when I do, I keep going that way. And I'll tell you something, hoss, I don't often make it to the local Sunday prayer meetings, but you can bet my Maker and I were having one whale of a conversation on the merits of whether or not I was going to finish the mission I was on in one piece. Now, I never was much of a smooth talker, but I must have said something to please Him just then, for I made it without a scratch!

I had my pistol in one hand, popping off shots at those braves behind the hides who were trying to do the same at me. The bucket was in my other hand. By the time I got to that well, I had it in mind that everyone in that area had their sights on me alone, as much lead as there was flying through the air. I pumped that handle like there wasn't any tomorrow and filled that bucket as full as I could before starting my run back to Charlie Myers's. But I made it! By God I did!!

I scooped up a handful of water myself as Bat found a cup and gave some to his friend. Seeing Billy Tyler lying there dying like that, as scared as I was I had a strange feeling for one moment, almost as if I knew exactly how Quanah Parker had felt that morning when he'd ridden into camp. Then a few more shots rang out in quick succession outside, and a strange knowing look came to Billy Tyler's face. He must have suddenly realized that the water didn't matter anymore, and his head slumped to the side in Bat Masterson's lap.

The boy was dead, but somehow I didn't think getting that water for him had been a wasted effort.

CHAPTER 11

"Anyone ever tell you you ain't too bright, Guns?" Colorado Johnny asked when I'd made my way back to Hanrahan's saloon.

"More times than I care to mention, son."

I tossed Hank his sixgun and grabbed my Sharps. "You'll have to reload that one, Hank." But Hard Luck Hank had other things on his mind just then.

"Why, you're a hero, Guns!" he said, his eyes near falling out of their sockets. "A genuine hero!" I paid little attention to him and went about reloading my own pistol until he prodded me some more. "Well, ain't you gonna say something, Guns?"

"Dime novels" was all I said, giving Johnny a glance and slowly shaking my head in disbelief. It wasn't what Hank wanted to hear, but it was the truth, because the boy spent his spare reading time devouring those worthless stories put out by Beadle and Adams. Worse yet, he probably believed them!

By mid-morning our attackers had eased up some, deciding to stay out of the range of our buffalo guns rather than risk any more gallant frontal attacks. That first one had been a doozy, but even though they had taken us by surprise, we had given them a good number of casualties to think about the next time they decided to test out their invincibility. Maybe the Great Spirits told those Indians they could come in and take us over, but when those Sharps started speaking, it was a whole new voice they were listening to. Yes, sir, it was a real mind changer.

When the sun hit high noon, the heathens had stopped charging us altogether and contented themselves with potshotting us from various positions behind everything from hides to wagons.

"You know, we're gonna need more ammunition pretty soon," one of the men remarked, and all of a sudden we were all checking our ammo pouches and agreeing with him.

"Trouble with that is most of the Sharps ammo is over at the Rath store," Hanrahan said.

"I'll go after it," Billy Dixon said. I might

have expected it from him.

"Suits me," Colorado Johnny said, picking up his Colt's. "When do you want to go?" he asked Dixon.

"Now's as good as any time." The other lad shrugged, and the two were soon out the door. Well, they were young.

A couple of others and I made trouble for a handful of braves hiding behind a stack of buffalo hides that Johnny and Billy were drawing fire from on their way to Rath's. Fact is, we gave those braves so much lead that they were soon doing their own fancy footwork trying to get the hell out of our range, especially after we shot their horses. It sure did seem like there was a lot of good horseflesh wasted that morning, but I reckon there are times you have to overlook that kind of slaughter.

Billy and Johnny had to get through a lot of gunfire, but they made it to Rath's all in one piece. We kept a watch out the side window and front door for the moment the two would return, knowing they would need as much cover coming back as they had going, and we were surprised to see only Johnny come running back. No one said anything, but I knew they were all wondering the same thing I was, whether Billy Dixon had been shot or had chosen to stay behind at Rath's.

We covered Johnny best we could, but for a moment it seemed like he faltered carrying those sacks of ammunition and nearly fell. Somehow he regained his footing and made it back. But when he got inside, I saw why it was he had almost gone down.

"My God, Johnny!" Sis yelled from the rear of the store, seeing the reddish flow trailing down his arm, as the rest of us did, and Billy Dixon was forgotten for the moment as Sis ran to Johnny's side and held on for dear life, just like I remembered her doing to me.

"You'll do him a lot more good if you get something to fix him up with, Sis," I said as I took one sack of ammunition from Johnny and Hank silently got the other.

"I could have done that, you know?" Even now there was still a jealous streak in Hard Luck Hank.

"Sure you could, Hank. Sure you could," Johnny said. He was trying to be accommodating, I guess, but Hank still had that look on his face and Johnny didn't need that just then. Not a-tall.

"Just shut up and get back to loading some guns, Hank." I said it in a way that let him know I didn't want any back talk. The look on his face didn't go away, but he did, and that was good enough, as Sis set down her medicinals and Jim Hanrahan offered the boy a cup of whiskey.

"You might as well numb your insides with this before she uses it on the outsides," he said with a smile.

It wasn't much more than a flesh wound, but sometimes even those can take the wind out of you if they hit you in the right spot. And Sis, well, I'll give her credit. She knew how to fix a man up when it came to doctoring; that she did. But Johnny wasn't feeling no pain, for between that liquor and having a chance to sit there and stare at Sis, he had himself pretty well occupied. Hank wasn't too far off and could see the looks they were exchanging as well as any of us, so I reckon if he didn't know by now just what the score was between those two kids . . . well, maybe he'd never learn.

You get a real interesting bunch of people in a group of buffalo hunters. Yes, you do. There are pilgrims like Hard Luck Hank, and young ones like Dixon and Masterson and Colorado Johnny just finding their place in this land. Then there are some who come out this way from the Midwest or back East to do some shooting, because they consider it a sport of some kind. Now,

I'll help out the youngsters as much as I can, because they deserve a chance, and without a doubt the ones with us that day had given a fine accounting of themselves. It was the sporting types I'd as soon feed to the wolves — or the Comanch' — but thankfully we had none there that day. The Hard Luck Hanks of the group, well, they had big dreams, which isn't all that bad, you understand. It's just that when you mix big dreams with a big mouth, you wind up with a big blowhard who claims he's going to do great things and seldom gets past the talking stage.

The rest of us, well, I reckon you could say we were as much a part of the land as the buffalo and Indians we shared it with. And somehow that made a big difference to us, for we considered it *our* land we were traveling, even though more of it was in turmoil, being fought over, than had been settled. Buffalo hunting was a way of life as much as it was a way of the land. Sort of grows on you like a winter coat in late autumn, if you know what I mean.

If you're going to survive in this country, one of the things you have to do is learn as much as you can about who you're sharing it with, whether your neighbor is an Indian or an immigrant, and whether you like him or not. More than a handful of us there that day had served with the Army as scouts or troopers at one time or another and had gotten to know the people out here as well as the land. So it wasn't any big surprise when we agreed that we knew who it was who had led the individual tribes in the early-morning frontal assault. We had seen Quanah Parker, who was leading the Comanche. Their cousins, the Kiowa, were led by Lone Wolf, another fearless chief who had a reputation for being his own man. The Cheyenne, who usually would have been outsiders to a confederation like the Comanche-Kiowa one, were being led by Stone Calf, who had yet another fierce reputation as a chief.

"Ask me, it's Stone Calf got 'em to start this fandango," I said as we discussed the situation.

"Why Stone Calf?" Colorado Johnny asked. He was going to turn out to be a right smart lad, this one, for he paid attention to most everything anyone said.

"He's Cheyenne, and they're as much cousin to the Arapahoe as the Kiowa are to the Comanch'."

"Oh," the boy said, his memory coming back, "you mean that massacre Custer did on the Washita back in '68."

"It's not just that, Johnny," Charlie Myers said. "That fool Chivington and his Third Colorado Volunteers started it back in '64 at Sand Creek. Helluva mess, they tell me."

"That's right," I confirmed. "My brother, Diah, was there, and he says they ain't got a straight story on that one yet."

"But that was ten years ago." Johnny didn't seem to believe that hatred could last that long.

"Way I got it figured, Johnny, most killing in this world ain't never been forgotten. People, they get real good at grudge fighting when it's one of their kin that's been done in. Hell, they might have hated his guts as much as the fella that killed him, but you can bet they're gonna go out after that fella anyway and get their piece of revenge."

"Sure don't seem right."

"Probably ain't. Still, when them sky pilots do their preaching, you're likely gonna hear 'em spouting off 'bout Cain and Abel, and son, that's going back some."

"Yeah" — Johnny shrugged — "there's that."

"I think you're both wrong," one hunter spoke up. "Come here a minute. I'll show you." He was standing next to one of the windows, a spyglass in his hand. "See that feller off on the knoll, yonder? Unless I miss my guess, that's Little Wolf. He'd be the medicine man of that war party, and if anyone could get 'em lathered up for a fight, it'd be him." The hunter smiled as he handed me the spyglass. "Course, you see how he's a-sitting off to the side of the battle 'stead of fighting it. Yup, them medicine men, they got 'em some brains."

I focused the glass and saw him sitting there as content as could be, all dressed up in his war paint, a good portion of which was yellow, taking in the battle while the chiefs he'd told were invincible were finding out differently. The gunfire and arrows seemed to have died down even more about then, so I hazed that looking glass along the horizon and wood line to see what I could see. Not that I expected to find anything, but there he was!

Quanah Parker!

I don't know what kind of description those Comanche have for what we call Sunday-go-to-meeting serenity, but that chief sure was basking in it. He didn't have a care in the world, but I had it in mind to change that real soon!

I grabbed up my Sharps and opened up the door, taking a few strides out front to get a firm stance. It was seven, eight hundred yards to where Quanah Parker sat his mount, but after a while you get used to Tennessee elevation and Kentucky windage in range shooting, so I took aim and squeezed off a shot. I had the empty shell flying out and was jamming in a second one before I noticed that I'd need one. Either my eyes were proving how old I really was, or I'd made a mistake in aiming, for the chief's horse had keeled over dead and thrown him to the ground in the process. Damn it, I'd hit the wrong target! Quanah was just getting up when I threw that second shot at him and thought I maybe hit him. Oh, he went down all right, but it wasn't flat on his back like you'd expect when you hit a man full in the front. He fell over to the side as if he'd been hit by a ricochet or a side shot — or he was faking it. I never would know, but that didn't seem to bother Hard Luck Hank, who was now standing by my side.

"That was a great shot, Guns!" he said excitedly.

"Think you could've made it?" I asked, wondering if he was still as wild about hunting Indians as he had been before.

"Oh, no, Guns, not me. But I wonder. . . ." His voice trailed off, but there was a serious tone in it now, one I'd not heard before.

"What's that, Hank?"

"Well, it just come to me." He squinted off in the distance, then scratched his head. "Do you figure that fella you just shot didn't realize he might get done in by a Big Fifty?"

"Beats the hell outta me."

"Or do you think he was committing suicide?"

I looked at Hank and, for the first time in a long time, gave out a laugh. What the hell, he might make it yet.

CHAPTER 12

It seemed eerie as hell that no one had shot at me while I'd been shooting Quanah Parker out of the saddle — in a manner of speaking, of course. You'd never get me to believe that the whole world was watching to see me make that one shot, so the shyness that our unfriendly visitors were showing now could mean only one thing. Their medicine had gone bad. The big chiefs were likely asking Little Wolf or whatever his name was what was making the medicine go sour now that they were well into the attack. I was putting my money on the reality of life, that being that no matter how much you believe in a higher being, the prospect of getting lead poisoning and dying from it is a strong deterrent to bravery — or foolishness — take your pick.

By midafternoon those young braves had gotten pretty unbrave and settled back around the foothills to the east and west of us. Fact is, they had gotten downright timid and were hardly even trying to potshot us anymore. And that, friend, can make you nervous. Not that we preferred being shot at, you understand, but there's something about total silence during a battle that tends to make you skittish as a newborn colt. In this case it meant one of two things. Either the fighting was over or those chiefs were calling another powwow to see if they couldn't fix up what was wrong with their medicine. And if that was the case, we all knew one thing for sure. There'd be one hell of a final attack, and it would be *our* bodies that were counted at the end instead of theirs. And considering that the medicine man who'd been spotted on the horizon earlier was no longer in sight, well, we started bracing ourselves for the worst.

"Oh, Johnny, I'm so scared," Sis said as she held on tight to the lad. If she was hanging on for dear life, it was for real this time, but then so was her need for Johnny. I reckon that's one thing you can count on. When you get put between a rock and a hard spot, you find out what a person is really made of.

"It'll be all right, hon." That Colorado Johnny, he'd do to ride the river with.

"You scared, Guns?" Hank asked.

"I'd be a damn fool or a liar, one, if I said I wasn't."

"Really?" He was astonished. "You admit to being scared!"

"Yeah," I said, cocking an eye toward him, "I admit to being scared. Scared to death, if you want to know the truth. Look, Hank," I said planting my hands on my hips the same way Pa had done when we were kids, "this ain't your dime novel West. People don't spend every day saving damsels in distress and then bragging about it at the local water hole. Out here you forget about trying to impress someone with how goddamn brave you are because . . . well, it just doesn't work! You want a man's respect, you'll stop talking and start doing, because the only thing cheaper than cheap whiskey is cheap talk, and the two seem to go together . . . if you recall." I was hoping he'd remember the incident that had taken place just before this fandango had started earlier that morning.

"Them dime novels are written by some fella back East who's likely got more imagination than Jim Bridger and Joe Meek thrown together, and according to Pa, those two were the biggest liars he'd ever seen! You get rid of that trash and start doing what's expected of you and you'll be a lot better off." I paused a moment and gave him a hard look. "By the way, Hank, are *you* scared?"

"Yeah," he replied, running a finger across his brow and pulling off the sweat. "Something fierce."

"That's as good a start as any."

It wasn't but a few minutes later that I was checking that Sharps for the I-don't-know-how-manyth-time when one of the men spoke up.

"Lookee here, boys," he said, peeking out the window. "Seems we got us some souvenir hunters."

"Looks more like scavengers to me," I said, joining him.

The Shadler Brothers had been killed in the early moments of the first and strongest attack on our camp. There had been so much going on then that none of us had noticed until afterwards that the Shadlers' wagon had been ransacked as well. Now, in the lull of the battle, a handful of warriors had snuck back to see what else they could take.

They were braves except for one who could have been a combination of damn near anything. He'd been spotted early in the fight, too, sitting off on a hill giving out bugle calls like you might expect from the cavalry. He had them down pat, and his main purpose seemed to be to distract us from the fighting going on while his compadres tried to make gone beaver out of us. He was dark enough to have been a Black, but some were saying he was a Mex or a cross between a Mex and an Indian. Those he'd come with had grabbed up baking powder, soap, bacon, and even some sugar and such and were about to make off with it. But a man's got his druthers, and it was this Bugle Boy that caught my eye in that moment. I made my way to the front door, kicked it open, and shot him square in the back as he was running away. He was dead before he hit the ground.

"What made you take aim on him?" Charlie Myers asked, following me out the door to check out the body.

"I've gone too many times in my life without it to not get a real appreciation for it, Charlie." He was still a bit puzzled by what I'd said, but when I pushed the can loose from the dead man's arm, I think Charlie knew what I meant.

What the Bugle Boy had been carrying off was a can of ground coffee.

Sometimes you get a strange feeling that comes over you and says things have changed. Charlie and I suddenly experienced it right then. Maybe it was because none of us had ventured out of the structures we called Adobe Walls that day without getting lead and arrows thrown at us. But now, now there wasn't anyone shooting at us. Charlie and I just gave each other strange looks, standing there like damn fools just waiting to be shot. But after a couple minutes, nothing happened, and soon there were others cautiously leaving the stores, as well as the saloon.

"How's Johnny?" a worried Billy Dixon asked, striding up. "Looked like he got hit carrying that ammunition back to you fellas."

"Just a flesh wound, Billy. His lady love fixed him right up." I gave him a mischievous wink, then felt my memory tug at me. "Say, son, how come you didn't return with Johnny?"

Dixon shrugged. "Rath's had all the forty-four ammunition, and they figured me for being one of the best shots in camp, so I stayed. You sure he's all right?"

"Now, son, does *that* look like a sick man?" I smiled as I glanced back toward the saloon door, where Johnny and Sis were sharing a kiss. I think that made Billy Dixon feel a whole lot better.

■ ■ ■ ■

We kept our rifles and pistols close at hand but began to mill about the camp to see what damage had been done. And when you think of what we'd been through that day, it didn't seem like much at all. Billy Dixon found that horse of his dead with an equally dead Indian brave next to it. He must have been trying to take the horse when he was killed, for the saddle had the scalp of a dead white woman and a fancy beaded piece of cloth stuck to it. A similar pair of items was found near another dead warrior who also carried a shield.

Seven Comanche and five Cheyenne bodies were found in or near the camp, though all of the wounded had been carried away. It didn't seem like many for all the shooting that had been going on that day, but I'd wager a season's pay that there were a lot of Comanche, Kiowa, and Cheyenne who were licking their wounds after tangling with us. The ones we found had died in awful strange ways, some of them. The most grotesque sight was that of a warrior who was discovered in back of a little sod house west of Rath's store. He was sitting upright against the wall, legs crossed as peaceful as could be; there wasn't a scratch on him, but his neck was broken. Seeing him like that made me not even want to guess at what had happened as a chill went down my spine.

Our only losses had been the Shadler Brothers and Billy Tyler, the lad I'd gotten water for. A few others had wounds. And that was a pretty damn good job of holding our own against three hostile Indian tribes.

Where we really took a loss was in the number of animals that had been killed throughout the day. All twenty-eight of the oxen the Shadlers had owned were just as dead as they were, not to mention fifty-some horses. The animals had been slaughtered by arrow or bullet, a dozen horses having fallen between the saloon and Rath's store. They would have to be gotten rid of or there would be one hell of a stink before long. But first we had some friends to take care of.

As a group, buffalo hunters were pretty much like those mountain men Pa had told me and my brother about. We'd band together to fight off some hostiles when the occasion called for it as it had done today, but basically we were loners who tended to our own business. I reckon that sounds kind of strange to citified folk, maybe even less civilized than they think we ought to be, but that doesn't mean we didn't feel it when one of our own got killed. I'd known the Shadlers even less than I'd known Billy Tyler, but I pitched right in that afternoon and did my share of the digging north of the corral to make the mass grave we lowered the three men into before sunset.

Tired as we were, there were a whole bunch of light sleepers in our camp that night. Normally, an Indian wouldn't do much fighting between sundown and sunup, but no one was about to forget the ordeal we'd been through. So we posted guards and said a silent prayer that the medicine man couldn't get the fight up in the braves by war-chanting that afternoon. Maybe that praying did some good, because that night turned out to be one of the quietest I'd been through in some time.

The stench of the dead horses was worse the next morning. The day was spent digging another massive grave and dragging what horses we could into it, then rolling the leftovers on to buffalo robes and hauling them away from camp.

"What about these dead Indians, Guns?" Hank asked late in the afternoon. "Ain't we gonna bury them, too?"

"What do you think, Charlie?" I asked

151

Myers, the man who'd hired me. "You feeling humane today?"

"Not hardly" was his only reply, and I knew he was feeling the same as I was and the rest who had dug the grave for our three friends the day before.

"There's your answer, Hank. Leave 'em to the buzzards and wolves."

"But they was humans, too, Guns. Don't they deserve —"

"Hank," I said, looking him hard in the face, "you lose a few friends like the men here have and *then* you come back and tell me about how human these birds are. Now, you just pull 'em over to where them dead horses are and leave 'em to the buzzards, *just like I said.*" Maybe ignorance being bliss is nice for newborn babies, but I'll tell you, hoss, when you've got to deal with it in people like Hard Luck Hank, it ain't nothing but a flat-out pain in the ass!

Once during that afternoon some of the men spotted a handful of warriors who stood up on a nearby hill and threw some lead at them to make them move, but that was the only sighting of the day. Of hostiles, at least.

Not long after that a couple of hunters showed up in a wagon from the north side and reported that they hadn't seen any sign of Indian activity at all in the last day or so.

Two more riders came in with the same report, and then another handful of Indians showed up on the horizon. As far away as they were, they didn't look like much. If what that fellow with the spyglass was saying was right, we'd sort of broken the spirit of the three tribes who had thought it was going to be so easy to wipe us out. The man was surveying the braves and had just mentioned that one of them was Little Wolf when Hard Luck Hank's Sharps boomed and one of the horses fell to the ground, the rider with it.

"By God, you got 'im!" the man with the spyglass said. "You got Little Wolf's horse!" The way he was jumping up and down, I do believe he would have done an Irish jig if someone'd had a fiddle to saw on.

"Huh?" True to form, Hank was confused.

"That medicine man has likely spent a good bit of his time these last few days convincing his chiefs how invincible they and their men are," I said. "Even now when they've lost some men, he probably had them convinced it was just a fluke and they're still as almighty powerful as ever, according to the Great Spirit."

"But what's that got to do with his horse getting shot?"

I shrugged. "What that medicine man does is pass on all his so-called powers to the chiefs and their warriors to make them as strong as he is. If he goes and gets himself shot horseless like he just did, it can mean only one of two things to those fellas riding with him. Either his medicine's gone bad, or . . ." I let it trail off for effect.

"Or what?"

"Or" — I smiled — "he's as big a liar as you tend to be at times, Hank." I didn't know how he would take it, but it didn't much matter to me.

"Yeah." He smiled back sheepishly. "I reckon that's so."

It looked like Hard Luck Hank was getting a sense of humor.

The evening meal was eaten in silence until Charlie Myers spoke what was on all our minds.

"We can't stay here forever."

"I was gonna ask what you folks are doing for horses now," one of the new arrivals asked innocently enough. But none of us needed to be told that we had next to nothing in the line of transportation.

"Sending someone to Dodge would be about the quickest way to get supplies and the Army down here for some protection," I said. When no one else spoke, I asked, "Any other suggestions?"

"I'll go," Hank said after another silence, and I don't mind telling you that it was a surprise to all of us!

"You?!" Charlie Myers and Colorado Johnny said the same thing at the same time but with a different meaning behind it. Charlie was just asking the question, while Johnny was more astonished by who had just volunteered than anything; but then he'd been working with Hank longer than any of us. Me, I raised an eyebrow and threw a suspicious glance at Hank.

"You sure you want to do this? Hell, are you sure you *can,* Hank?" I'd never once seen him watch his back trail on the way down here, and that can make all the difference in the world to a man, because things don't look the same when you're going in the opposite direction, be it the Santa Fe, Oregon, Chisholm, or that piddly trail we'd followed from Dodge. That might have been a small detail to consider, but it was an important one if you were putting all your chips on one man to come through for you.

"Well, you said I ought to be doing instead of talking, so I'm willing to give it a try. Honest, Guns, I ain't gonna let you down." He lowered his voice as though what he was

155

about to say he wanted to be just between the two of us. "I don't often do it, but I'll give you my word on it. I'll make it through."

"Now you think you can say it loud enough to be heard by the rest of these folks?" I asked him outright.

"I'll" — for a second he nearly lost his voice — "I'll make it through. I ain't gonna disappoint none of you."

They took him at his word, and an hour later, I was helping him get ready for his ride. He had two pistols, a rifle, and a horse with bottom to get him to Dodge. I was just hoping Hank had the same kind of bottom if he didn't have an easy ride.

"Those folks are counting on you, son," I said, trying to be as encouraging as I could. "You do most of your riding at night and keep your eye on the North star and you'll make it all right. And when you get there, Hank, you find you a good beefsteak and have 'em tally it to my bill."

"You mean it, Guns?" His eyes lit up with pride.

"Sure thing, kid."

He was almost ready to go when I spotted that mischievous look he got — used to get — when he was ready to play a prank on someone.

"What do you think would happen, Guns, if I didn't make it through, didn't head for Dodge? Would they understand, do you think?" He was starting to feel gamey again, and that wasn't what he was going to need to get through a hundred-and-fifty-mile ride. I reckon there are ways I could have gotten the message across to him, but it's the truth that always best makes a believer out of you.

"Well, Hank, I'll tell you," I said, pushing my hat back on my head. "We've got a pretty rough lot of people here at Adobe Walls, but I reckon they got as much forgiveness in them as anyone, for a good cause. So if you was to ride out of here and not head for Dodge . . . well, if the Comanch' came back and tried doing us in again there'd be a few of us that would survive, and I reckon if we found you, we'd be forgiving and all, just like I said." I gave him my own mischievous smile to let him know he was in trouble. "But you've got to remember one thing, kid."

He cleared his throat the way he'd done when he volunteered for the mission.

"What's that, Guns?"

"They, we, *I* wouldn't forgive you until *after* we'd hung you."

He cleared his throat again and gave a

weak smile.

"I was just joshing you, Guns."

"I know, Hank. I know. Now, get the hell outta here and let's hope the next time we meet its under more pleasant circumstances."

And he did.

The second day after the battle, we started building up the stores and making better defensive positions out of what little we had. It's surprising how much imagination most people have when they come upon hard luck and are forced to work together. I heard some fancy educated man back East say it built character. Real wordy he was. If I ever meet him again, I'll have to ask him about that phrase. All I knew was we were working together for a common cause — staying alive! — and if you want to get something done right, well, that's the best way to do it out here.

More hunters started drifting in, and I think it was that day the Comanche and their compadres got it through their heads that we weren't moving unless we wanted to.

That Billy Dixon wasn't but half my age, which explains the sharpness of his eyes. And how he did it is still beyond me, but I can't say as I've seen a better shot. You see, it was that morning that some fifteen warriors rode up on the bluff east of Adobe Creek. I don't know if it was because he was still feeling the loss of his good friend Billy Tyler or what that made him do it, but he picked up his brand new .44 Sharps, got a clear view and a good stance, aimed, and fired. Now, hoss, that was a good fifteen hundred yards he shot across, but it don't matter whether you call it luck or damn good shooting, one of those young bucks flew out of the saddle just like he'd been chest shot only a hundred yards off!

"Too bad Hank didn't see that shot," I said, remembering the comment Hard Luck Hank had made about one of my shots the day of the battle.

"Why's that?" young Billy asked.

"That was suicide" was all I said with a smile.

Billy Dixon's shot was what you'd call the end of the Battle of Adobe Walls, I reckon. *Our Adobe Walls!*

CHAPTER 13

By the sixth day after the battle, we had Adobe Walls as fortified as we could make it, in case of another Indian attack. We had also grown in ranks to about a hundred men, all heavily armed and ready for a fight. We were still hoping Hard Luck Hank had made it through to Dodge and that some kind of relief was on the way, but even then it seemed fairly certain that the hostiles who had come at us nearly a week earlier were no longer in the area. Word was filtering in from hunters who joined us that those same Indians had been seen to the south in Texas and that they had killed thirty more whites and were heading west to do more plundering. In effect we were safe from further attacks.

"So you're getting restless, too, huh?" Colorado Johnny said to me at the end of the sixth day.

"That noticeable, is it?"

"Arm's a lot better." He smiled rolling his shoulder some. "Besides, I'm getting that way myself."

"Jim Hanrahan's been talking 'bout getting a bunch of us together and heading up to Dodge," I remarked.

"Don't think Hank made it through, does he?"

Sending an unproven pilgrim like Hard Luck Hank on a mission like we had was enough to give anyone doubts as to how successful he'd been. I'd seen Pony Express riders who did a hundred miles in a day's time easy, but they were riding relays. Other riders would push their mounts as far and as fast as they could go without caring whether the horse dropped dead at the end of the journey or not, and that was a shame, it purely was. As for Hank, hell, I figured that riding ten miles a day was as far as he could stretch that mustang we'd put him on, and at that rate it would take him two weeks to get to Dodge if he played it right. And if he was taking his time, I didn't figure we'd ever have occasion to see him again to cuss him out, at least not alive.

"What do *you* think?" I asked.

"I don't know, Guns." Johnny squinted, rubbing his jaw like some old-timer thinking up a story. "Ordinarily I'd say no, he didn't make it, but seeing him during and after that battle the other day . . . well, I sort of got the feeling he changed some. He sure was honest about wanting to make that ride when he volunteered." Johnny paused and looked up at me. "I think he did, Guns. I think he made it. Unlucky as he tends to be, I just hope he made it in one piece."

By the end of the day, about twenty-five of us had decided to leave the next morning for Dodge, Hanrahan, Dixon, Colorado Johnny, and me included. We'd had time enough to round up the horses that had been run off during the battle and to borrow what we didn't have, so that was no problem. As for weaponry, let's just say we could have opened up our own armory between the Sharps buffalo rifles, various and assorted pistols, bowie knives, and shotguns. Armed to the teeth is what we were.

We rode at a steady pace, and everything went fine until the second day, when we came upon San Francisco Creek and the remains of what had once been a buffalo hunter. I forget what his name was, but it's just as well, because he'd been mutilated something fierce, and from the looks of him it must have been about the same time we'd been under siege at Adobe Walls. Burying the remains of the poor devil wasn't the easiest task any of us ever did, and you can bet this whole experience was having an effect on us, a definite effect.

"You notice how brackish that water tasted this morning?" Johnny asked the following day. "Had a terrible taste to it."

"I know," I said. "Never changes."

"Never changes? You been to this creek that often?"

"Oh, it's not the water in the creek, Johnny. That's good as it ever was. Next time you come through, you'll taste it better."

A frown crossed his brow as he tried to understand what it was I was talking about.

"It's your system does it to you." I went on. "Food ain't got much taste, and water's brackish no matter whose well you take it from. General revolt, I reckon it is."

"Revolt?"

"Death, son, death. There's damn few of us ever get used to seeing death at work, and our system reminds us how bad it is . . . at least until something else comes along to take our attention." I glanced over at him and nodded. "Yeah, the water was a mite brackish today."

We rode on in silence most of the rest of the trip to Dodge.

Pa said that when you fought a war, no matter whether it was against Indians, Mexicans, or whomever, you'd come away alive if you were a survivor. Trouble was, he claimed, no matter how alive you were when the war was over, there was always a little bit of you that died inside. I'd warred with them all, Mexicans and Indians, and some I couldn't describe if I wanted to, and I was feeling the same way on this ride back to Dodge as I had at the end of those other wars, short or long as they had been. I was a big man, and I knew I could hold my own against more than most, but I also knew that I wasn't so cold-blooded that I could massacre a bunch of people and walk away from it and order a good cut of meat to dine on in the next ten minutes. It was a hard land we lived in all right, and it took a hard man to make the span from birth to death cover forty or fifty years, which is what I was working on right then. But I had to stop and wonder sometimes if it was worth it if what you wound up with was ice in your veins because that was the only way you could stay alive and keep your sanity.

I reckon that's what I'd been trying to explain to Colorado Johnny, as clumsy as my words were. I'd taken a liking to the boy and thought he and Sis could make a good life together. But he'd have to know how to get past the hard times like these without drying up inside like I figured I sometimes had, for without that kind of strength, their love wouldn't last.

Yes, the water had tasted sort of brackish.

"See, Guns, I told you I'd make it! Told you I would!" Hard Luck Hank was excited as could be to see us ride into town.

"So you made it back," I said, dismounting in front of Fat Jack's saloon. "Ain't nobody brought relief down to us that I know of."

"Sure they did!" he said confidently. "Sure they did! You had to see 'em, Guns! Why, Tom Nixon rounded up forty men soon's I got here and moved out south! You *had* to have seen 'em, Guns!" The way he was spitting everything out all at once without a hem or a haw, it was likely he was telling the truth.

"They didn't go down the same trail we did, then," I said.

"We probably passed each other a few miles apart," Johnny offered for an excuse.

"Could be, Guns," Billy Dixon added.

"How long'd it take you to get here?" I asked Hank directly.

"Three-and-a-half days," he said proudly.

"You can ask anyone here."

He'd done some changing all right. Maybe actually doing something worthwhile in his life had given him a new outlook on things. He was standing up for himself instead of making excuses for what he'd done, and that was as good a start as any. Maybe there was hope for the lad.

"Looks like you were right, Johnny," I said, glancing to my side.

"What's Guns talking about?" I never have seen a man who took it peaceful like when he found out others had been talking about him, particularly when what they'd been saying may not have been all that flattering, and Hard Luck Hank was no exception.

"Wel-l-l," Johnny said, drawing it out, "there was some speculation on whether you'd make it back in one piece or not."

"You sure it wasn't whether I'd come back at all?" Hank asked, getting a bit riled.

"Of course not, Hank," I said, trying to soothe him down. "It's just that you were covering a rough piece of prairie, what with all those hostiles hunting scalps around here now. Hell, any other man might not have made it." I placed a hand on his shoulder like I remembered Pa doing to us boys as youngsters, hoping he'd feel the same way we had back then. "You done fine, Hank, and I'm real proud of you for it. Shows you got the makings. And I ain't funning you when I say that."

Fat Jack stuck his head out over the batwing doors of his establishment before Hank could respond. "You know, fellas," he said, "I've got a whole barful of beers just sitting here getting warm. You jaw much longer, they's gonna lose all their flavor, period."

"Man's right," Jim Hanrahan said. "We got plenty of time to palaver." He headed toward the saloon, stopped briefly to tell Hank he appreciated what he'd done, and went in. Most of the others followed his lead, a few even inviting Hank in for a drink or two on them. When they had all gone into the saloon, only Johnny and I were left on the boardwalk.

"Looks like you were right, son."

"Yeah," Johnny said, "old Hank's taken a change for the better, I'd say. Why, pretty soon I'll bet you'll even be liking him, Guns."

I pushed the hat back on my head, and smiled.

"Tolerate him, maybe. Like him?" I shook my head. "I don't know if I'm ready for that yet. Let's get these horses took care of. They been working a damn sight harder than we have."

I got cleaned up so I at least looked presentable enough to stop in at one of the better eateries for a meal. I was still wearing the same buckskins but had shaved and washed off the top layer of dirt from my face and hands.

The first thing I did when I entered the place was see if Hard Luck Hank had taken me up on that beefsteak I'd told him to order once he'd made Dodge.

"And then some, sir," the owner, a medium-built English-accented fellow said. "As I recall, he's been in here at least once a day since he returned to have a cut of our prime beefsteak."

"That's Hank," I said, remembering that there are some things you won't ever change in a man. So I simply smiled and told the man I'd pay for them. I figured what the hell, I'd rather be paying the four-bit high-way robbery they charged for fancy meals in this place than for a pine box for boot hill.

I took a seat and was immediately in trouble. A couple of range hands who looked like they'd overdone it shopping for the citified clothes they wore gave me a bothersome look. When one of them started sniffing the air for some foul odor and acting as though they'd found it, I shrugged my shoulders.

"Kinda ripe, ain't it?" I said, smiling. "Just got in off the trail and ain't had time to get cleaned up." A simple explanation ought to be enough, for these two had no doubt seen hard times themselves and ought to understand.

"No," the other one said, sniffing again and making a face. " 'Tain't the range smell. It's the yellow smell."

"What was that?" I asked, wondering just what was going on.

"Say, I'll bet you're one of them buffalo hunters claims he was down south and couldn't defend hisself proper."

"Mister," I said, "I'm tired. I ain't had a decent meal in I don't know how long, and that's the only thing I came in here for." I wanted to overlook his back talk, I really did.

First one got up, then the other, as they slowly walked to my table, making those silly faces as they did so.

"Heard they was afraid of a bunch of Injuns, no less."

"Heard they couldn't defend theyselves for nothing," the other said in a mean voice. "Never did care for buffalo hunters."

"That's too bad, mister, cause Guns Hooker is one of the best," Hard Luck Hank said from the doorway. For an instant it crossed my mind that if Hank hadn't been there, I might have avoided a fight, but then it didn't seem to matter, because these hard-cases were going out of their way to start something.

"Shut up, sonny."

Hank said nothing as he walked toward the two.

"You know, gents," I said, pushing back my chair and rising to my full height, "I really am tired. Now, maybe you figure that going after a man when he's played out gives you an advantage, and that may be." I poked one of them in the chest, pushing him back a ways toward the entrance. "But you ought never to discount the mad factor." I gave him another shove, pushing him further back.

"Sirs, please, no fighting in here," the owner said in a pleading way.

"Wouldn't think of it," I said to him, but it was the plug ugly before me I was looking at. "There was a thousand in that *bunch* of Indians, mister, and twenty-eight of us to start with. They tried doing us in, but it was the mad factor that kept us going. You see, pilgrim, once you get a man mad, it don't matter how tired he is; he'll fight you." I had him within six feet of the entrance door now, containing my anger as best I could. "Like I said, I'm tired . . . but you just made me mad, too."

I hit him hard below the belt, then drove another right into his gut as he folded in two. Pulling back a fistful of hair brought him upright again quick, which is when I hit him with a fast left and a hard right that sent him flying back through the doorway. He was out cold.

To my surprise, Hard Luck Hank had taken a poke at the other troublemaker. Trouble was the fellow was a mite bigger than Hank. He had Hank on the floor and was about to stomp him when I gave him the same treatment his partner got, a couple of quick punches that left him on the floor. I didn't have the Big Fifty with me then or I would have knocked him out with a butt stroke. As it was, he was reaching for some kind of hideout gun he had on him.

But he never made it.

"Tut, tut, now, friend," Colorado Johnny said, appearing in the doorway, his Colt's in his fist, "you remember what Mama said about having manners at the dinner table." That arm of his might have been a little sore, but that boy could snake a pistol out of nowhere like you wouldn't believe. When the ruffian made no move to remove his hand from the inside of his coat, Johnny pointed the sixgun at the man's nose, cocking it. "You bring your hand out from that coat anything but empty, and you're going to have a second hole in you to get rid of all that manure you're made of." He smiled the way a man does who has the upper hand and knows his opponent knows it.

It seemed to take a long time, but the hand came out slowly and empty as the man got to his feet.

"Told you there wouldn't be no fighting in here," I said, hoping the owner noticed that there hadn't been any furniture busted up. "If I was you, though, I'd be more particular about who I let in the place."

My opponents sure were quiet when they were the ones on the dirty end of the stick, because neither one said anything to that. Not that the one I'd knocked out would have been able to say much, for I had a hunch I'd done his jawline a bit of rearranging when I'd hit him. Still, Johnny didn't put his pistol away until the two were out of sight.

"You're getting a habit of showing up at the right time, son," I said to him.

"Actually, Hank was going to show me

where he's been eating the last few days," he replied. "Claims they got right tasty food here."

They joined me for a meal, but it was Hank who seemed to be the one who was the most worked up about something. Even in making small talk, he was anxious, I could tell, to get around to one subject in particular, and he finally spit it out.

"Ain't you excited?" he asked, addressing both of us. Johnny and I exchanged glances.

"About what?"

"Why, getting reoutfitted and going back out for the buffalo, of course!" I reckon people get carried away when they're infatuated with something before they find out what it really involves. And if Hard Luck Hank ever did get to take part in a buffalo hunt, he was going to discover that it wasn't anything like his dime novels made it out to be.

"No," I said, "as a matter of fact I ain't, Hank. Come to think of it, you ask any of the men who came in with us, and you'll likely get the same answer."

"But how could that be?" he said, dismayed.

"Maybe you don't understand, Hank. Hunting them buffalo, well, we're taking away the red man's supply of meat; the herd's getting thinner each year. You may not know it, but it wasn't just a coincidence that they rode down on us there at Adobe Walls. They knew we were hunters, and killing us all was their way of keeping the food they figure they need so badly. Now, they didn't do nearly all the damage they wanted to, but you can bet they made it clear that if we show up there again, they'll be right there with the same welcoming committee to do the same thing all over, and I don't know about you, but I ain't too keen on living through that foofaraw again."

"You mean there ain't going to be no hunt this year?" I'd say Hank was about as heartbroke then as Colorado Johnny would be if Sis was to leave him.

"I don't think so, Hank."

"But . . . what are you going to do?!"

"I ain't sure, Hank," I said, "but right now I want to eat a decent meal."

CHAPTER 14

Actually, I wasn't all that worried about money, but it did bother me some as to what I was going to do for wages this season. Not that I was lazy or anything, you understand, but it was my policy to get the most money for the least amount of work in as short a time as possible. That may make me sound like Hard Luck Hank all over again, but I ain't. I'd hunted buffalo the past few years and made enough money in one summer to last me the rest of the year. I'd marshaled for a couple of towns out here for a hundred a month and even done a bit of bounty hunting. Like I said, being the hunter has a decided effect over being the huntee. One of those fancy fellows back East that had to have a Webster's and an encyclopedia to explain things proper called it being *versatile;* to me it wasn't nothing more than being handy, plain and simple.

Anyway, it was when I headed for what

once had been my sleeping quarters and remembered they had been busted up that my memory got a jog and it hit me that I'd nearly forgotten about that diamond I was carrying in my Sharps! That had to be worth a hell of a lot of money, especially if Fat Jack's brother-in-law still wanted it back as badly as he had a couple of months before. When I turned in that night at Joshua's livery, I made a mental note to check with Jack the following day about the stolen gems.

I bought some new denims and a couple of work shirts the next morning and headed for the barbershop to get sheared and to see if there was still a bathtub in the back that rented out for two bits an hour. The barber wrinkled his nose at me, said he thought he saw something crawling around in my hair, and recommended I take the bath first. At first I thought he figured me for being too ripe to stand next to, but it turned out he was right about something having taken root on my head beside my hair. I decided I'd burn my old clothes as soon as I was done.

I was sitting there enjoying the warm water when I heard the back door open. I had a bar of soap in one hand, but when

Colorado Johnny walked in, he was looking down the barrel of my CSA cavalry-model pistol.

"Sometimes it's best to announce yourself, kid," I said, lowering the pistol. "It makes for a longer lifetime."

"I'll make a note of it," he said, swallowing hard. Then he smiled. "You're about as jumpy as that Meagher marshal over Wichita way."

"Lately it's getting to be a way of life."

Mike Meagher and his twin brother sort of ran Wichita those days. Mike did the marshaling, while his brother filled in as mayor, and they were probably two of the best examples of honest men to come along in some time. So far Mike had killed only one man, in what was likely the strangest gunfight that had ever taken place. Seems one fellow came in to town every Saturday, got drunk, raised Hail Columbia, and got locked up for the night. Sometimes he put up a fuss about it, and after getting buffaloed by the marshal more times than he cared for, he decided to put an end to the local law one Sunday morning when he got released from the hoosegow. Trouble was he wasn't much of a gunman, so he wasn't about to take on Mike Meagher face-to-face. Instead, he walked out back, where

Mike was taking his morning constitutional, and fired six shots into the crapper! Like I said, this fellow had troubles, one of them being he couldn't shoot worth a damn, because Mike didn't even get a scratch. Mike, he kicked open the door and shot the sonofabitch once and put an end to the whole thing! It was probably the one gunfight that took place inside and outside a crapper. But it wasn't Mike Meagher's life I was concerned about just then. It was my own.

"Thought you might've been those two birds who tried raising a ruckus last night. They looked like the type who'd be sore losers," I said.

"You got that right, Guns." Johnny ran a hand across the back of his neck, apparently as mystified as I was about the whole incident of the night before. "From what I seen, they set out to prod you, all right. It's just that the whole thing seemed so . . . so . . ."

"Dime novel," I said.

"Yeah, that's it! Hell, most folks hereabouts figure we done right well down at the Walls, everything considered. But those two." He shrugged. "I don't know. I can't explain it."

I'd scrubbed another layer of dirt off

178

before a notion crossed my mind. The fight I'd had with Lance Carver had seemed much the same! It had struck me funny then and looked ever more suspicious now.

"Did Carver have any others he hung around with?" I asked. He had always seemed like a loner to me, but you never could tell about a man's past, especially if he was from three counties over.

"No, not that I recall," Johnny said. "There were times he said he had business to take care of, times he didn't want me around, but —" A spark of recognition hit him, and I was sure he'd just come to the same conclusion I had. "Say, you don't think those two last night were maybe Carver's friends, do you?" he asked.

"I was thinking more along the line of business associates."

The boy had brains and guts and had proved himself on more than one occasion. For me that was enough to confide in him. After all, I'd taken him on as a partner of sorts even if there wouldn't be any buffalo hunt this season. Besides, as bright as he was, maybe he could shed some more light on this whole thing.

"Close that door and hand me some of that hot water, Johnny. I've got one more layer of dirt to get off of me . . . and one helluva story to tell you." Then I told him about the diamond in the saddlebags, my suspicions . . . everything.

I was getting my hair cut when Johnny ran into the barbershop, an excited expression on his face. There was only one thing that could give him a look like that, and I did my best to prepare myself. Sis followed Johnny in, close on his shirttail and still dressed in that fancy getup of hers.

"Guess who just come into town!" he said quickly.

"Lessen it's someone besides Sis here, I'd hardly say you've given me much of a choice."

"That relief party Hank said Tom Nixon took down to the Walls, well, it got there not long after we left," he spouted off, near out of breath. "Cissy came on ahead with one of the boys, and the others'll be back in Dodge in a day or so."

"So we got rescued after all," I said, but what was going through my mind was that I might start putting some trust in Hard Luck Hank after all. "Glad you made it back in one piece, Sis."

"Not half as glad as I am." She smiled, giving Johnny's hand a squeeze. "Johnny and I have some talking to do. Real serious talking." She was getting moon-eyed now, leaving me no doubt as to what kind of talking it would be.

"Well, that's why I came right over, Guns," Johnny said.

"You'll have to pardon me now, kids," I said quickly, pulling off the doodad the barber had covering me. I reached for my hat, glancing in the mirror as I did so. "I'll come back for the sides later," I told the barber, and tossed him a coin before leaving.

It's not that I'm totally against marriage, you understand. It's just that for some people it's right, and for others it ain't, and I've always felt like one of the ain'ts. Fact is, I've always stayed away from marriages, wedding ceremonies, and them fancy little parties they have afterward as well. It's probably the only superstition I've ever had in my life. So just to make it look like I did have business to attend to, I walked over to Fat Jack's and ordered a beer. It was one of the places I'd told Johnny I planned on checking that day, anyway, when I'd told him the story of what had happened to me.

"You're getting yourself quite a reputation, Guns," Jack said, wiping the bar.

"How's that?"

"After you done in that Carver fella and

the word got around, why, that brother-in-law of mine — the fella owns the jewelry store? — he came a-asking for you."

"Why so?" If I sounded overly curious, it was because I was.

"Why, he thinks Carver was in on the scheme to steal his valuables." Jack set another beer before me. "I heard the marshal wasn't too keen on what you done, but my brother-in-law Asa, he thinks you done the city a service. Yes, he does."

"He wanted to tell me that in person, did he?"

Jack shrugged. "I reckon so. He said the next time I saw you, I should tell you he'd like to parlay with you." Then he gave me the location of Asa's store and said the drinks were on the house.

If there is something about store clerks and bank tellers that people fix in their minds, it's the way they look. The men are either short and fat or tall and skinny and nearly always balding. Their wives are usually pudgy and tending toward ugly, which is likely how their husbands got bald in the first place. Straight out of a Dickens book, they are. Asa Turner didn't turn out to be much different, even as the owner, proprietor, and only clerk of the jewelry shop, a tall thin man with a receding hairline and a suspicious look about him. If he ever smiled, it was probably to have a picture taken for the family album, and he didn't look like a family man.

"I'm Matt Hooker," I said, sticking a paw out. "Fat Jack said you were looking for me."

"Yes." Turner's face held more of a squint than a smile, the kind a businessman will give you to let you know this is *only* business. For a short moment I wondered if maybe Jack wasn't playing a joke on me.

"I understand that you're quite a . . . desperado," Turner said, hunting for the right word.

"You've got to be careful how you pick your words, Mister Turner. I'm not a desperado. On the other hand, I let it be known that I ain't one to tangle with."

"One's as good as the other to me, Mister Hooker." He was real practical, this man. "Especially your kind," he added with an uppity kind of sneer.

"That so." I raised an eyebrow in casual interest, feeling inside like I could learn to dislike this pilgrim real easy. Real easy. Fact is, I was getting the urge to give the bastard a lesson in what I meant by my not being one to tangle with.

"I'll get right to the point," Turner said.

"Ain't met a businessman yet that didn't."

183

"The jewelry that was stolen from me a few months ago — you're familiar with that robbery?" All of a sudden he was cautious, as if trying to get the honey out of a nest without bothering the bees.

"Seems to me I heard about it, yeah. Why do you ask?"

"A number of jewels were stolen. One of them was a diamond that was quite expensive, worth several thousand dollars. I'm willing to pay you five hundred dollars if you can find the men who stole that gem." He shrugged, giving me that phony smile. "I'd even settle for just getting the diamond back."

"Five hundred? That's an impressive offer."

"Yes, sir. I thought it would interest you."

"Oh, it does, friend, it does." I couldn't deny that I hadn't been offered money like that any too often in my life. And he was expecting me to take it, so I did.

"All right, Mister Turner, you've got a deal," I said. "Though I might have some trouble in locating those birds. For all I know, they could be down in Mexico by now."

"I suppose that could be true. But go where you must to get them — to get it — back. If it's money you lack for ammunition and supplies, I'll advance it to you."

"Do that, would you?" I was getting real curious now.

"Of course! I want that diamond back!"

To say he was frantic about it would be putting it mildly. But then, I reckon people who are as possessive as these town folks were get that way.

"All right, friend, all right," I said, holding up a passive hand. "You just settle down, and I'll see what I can do. Tell you what. In about an hour or so, why don't you bring a couple of boxes of Sharps fifties over to Fat Jack's. He's got a lunch counter, and I ought to be ready to travel by then."

"Splendid. I'll be there."

I didn't know how Jack could tolerate Asa Turner, as a brother-in-law or as a person, for the man was quite rude in his manners and speech. That last comment he'd made was accompanied by a sort of sigh of relief, as far as I could tell, almost as if he'd thought I'd be bartering with him for a higher price. But five hundred dollars was a lot of money for anyone in those days — damn near a year's worth of living money — so what the hell.

"That's Asa," Fat Jack said a half hour later when I pulled my horse up in front of his saloon and related my conversation with his brother-in-law as he poured me a beer. "Tightest man with money I ever seen since Pa read me that story about that Scrooge fella. He salts it all away someplace and gets real offensive if you ask what kind of a profit he made this week."

"Maybe he ain't making a profit."

"Oh, no," Jack said, shaking his head with a smile. "If there's a profit to be made, you can bet Asa'll find it. Put it this way, Guns. He can sniff out money the way you can find them buffalo."

"Then he's having a better season than I am this year."

Colorado Johnny came in a few minutes later while I was eating at the lunch counter. "Say, Guns, do you think you've got the time to talk over what Cissy and I were wanting to tell you a while back?" He was still as good-humored as he'd been when Sis had ridden into town earlier in the morning, and I was glad for him, I really was. But I also felt a chill running down my spine when he mentioned her. It could only mean wedding bells the way they looked at each other, and to tell the truth, hoss, for an instant there I was almost wishing I was back at Adobe Walls! That's how much I dislike weddings! But I was just putting off what needed to be said, so I decided to break it to him right then.

"Might as well, I reckon." I finished the sandwich and the beer while he spit out his proposition.

"Cissy and me, we'd like you to be our best man at our wedding," he said with all the blush of a schoolboy asking the neighbor's daughter to dance at the Sunday social.

"No." I never was known for having any tact, and I was damned if I was going to start now, so I told him flat-out.

"But Guns, I thought —"

"You thought wrong, son. Weddings are bad luck for me, so I stay away from 'em." All of a sudden I was looking into eyes that were as sad as a dog after he's been kicked by the town bully. You'd have thought the boy had lost every friend he had in the world. "Look, Johnny, you go ask Hank; he's taken a liking to you. And if he can't do it, I'll think about it."

That perked him right up.

"Gee, thanks, Guns! Cissy's really gonna like that!"

"Remember, I said I'd *think* about it. I didn't say I'd *do* it."

"Sure, Guns, I understand," he said, grinning from ear to ear. "Wait'll I tell —"

"As a matter of fact, you *can* wait," I said,

grabbing his arm before he left.

"Wait?" He looked puzzled, which, I suppose, was to be expected.

"You remember that story I told you this morning?"

"Yeah, sure."

"How'd your Mister Odom do at teaching you spelling?"

"Fine, I reckon. Real good."

"Then I want you to go down to the telegraph office," I said, and filled him in on my plan.

Asa Turner was coming in at the same time Colorado Johnny left. He carried two boxes of cartridges with him but looked as if he felt more awkward walking into Fat Jack's saloon than he did about carrying the ammunition. He was probably used to fancy sipping whiskey rather than the bar whiskey Jack was making a living selling.

"Here is the ammunition you requested." Turner set the boxes atop the bar, still all business and formality. He didn't order a drink, and I don't believe any of the handful of men in the place would have offered to buy him one.

"Nice to see you, Asa," Jack said with a weak smile. One thing I'll say for Fat Jack, he went out of his way to be friendly to folks, which is likely why he did such a good business. And he'd tried to be as fair as he could about his brother-in-law, but from the way the expression on his face was changing now, I'd bet two-to-one odds he'd dig Asa Turner's grave and toss him in it and bury him alive all just to see the man squirm. Come to think of it, I'd do the same my own self.

"Yes, how quaint." You couldn't tell if Turner was talking about Jack's bar or the fact that he'd walked into the place and actually spoken to his brother-in-law. Apparently he was used to giving orders, too. "Mister Hooker, I would suggest —"

"You know, friend," I said, cutting him off, "I've been a mite curious about something."

"Really." He didn't seem to care much about what I thought, but then some bosses are like that. "Since I am the one who's paying you, Mister Hooker —"

"That's just what I've been curious about, friend. I'm wondering why it is you picked me to go after your jewels."

"My brother-in-law said you were a strong, hard man and that you had a reputation. Now then, Mister Hooker, if you *don't* think you can do the job —"

"Oh, I can do the job, hoss. I can do the job."

I think I had him riled enough to make some kind of smart-ass remark, but he never got the chance to say it, at least not to my face. A series of gunshots rang out not far down the street, and we all looked at one another in that instant, asking ourselves if someone was having fun or if there was danger in the air.

"The bank's been —" someone yelled before another shot cleared the air and he was silenced. Then there was the brief sound of horses milling about, and I grabbed up my Sharps and threw back the batwing doors as two riders flew by in a heap of dust.

"It's the bank! It's been robbed!!" someone down the street shouted.

I would have taken a shot, but the riders turned a corner and were gone. And in one ear I could hear Asa Turner yelling at me.

"It's them! I saw them! They're the ones who took my jewelry! After them, you fool! After them!!"

CHAPTER 15

I ignored Turner for the moment and ducked back into the saloon to pick up my shells.

"Bank's been robbed, Jack," I said. "Where's the local law?"

"Up north, I think," he replied. "Had a prisoner to pick up, is what the marshal said. Be back tomorrow, I reckon."

"I insist that you go after those men!" Turner was shouting at me again. And that tore it!

"You're an awful mouthy little bastard," I said, setting the shells down and taking a fistful of his coat front. "Now, if you want to keep on being able to talk, mister, you'd better stop flapping them lips of yours, 'cause if you don't it's gonna be them and your gums that's all you'll have left in that part of your face, money or no money."

As soon as I let go of him, Jack grabbed ahold of his shoulder and had no trouble leading him over to a chair. Jack plunked him down and began cussing at him something fierce, which, I do believe, is something he'd wanted to do for years.

In the meantime I left the saloon, shoved the boxes inside my saddlebags, and mounted my horse, steering him over to the crowd that had gathered in front of the bank. There on the boardwalk was the body of the man, a teller, who had first run out of the bank to set off the alarm. He hadn't made it, though, for a bullet through the heart had silenced him, as was evidenced by the spreading pool of blood on his shirtfront.

"Get some men together," I said. "Have 'em follow me —"

I would have said more, but another alarm went up, this one for a fire that had been started in the livery not far off. Horses were running wild, and I knew a good share of the town would be needed to douse a fire that big before it spread to other buildings and put the whole town in flames. Realizing it was hopeless to ask for volunteers right now, I wheeled my horse around and headed out of town.

The side street the robbers had taken was due west, but once out of town, they had turned south, just as I'd figured. For some

reason or other everyone heads south whenever something goes sour on them. I don't
know if it's because they figure that there's
all those pretty señoritas to take care of
them south of the border or that things are
cheaper there or what, but they go. I found
it especially difficult to believe that anyone
would leave Dodge City for Mexico, even
with a fistful of dollars. Hell, you had to go
through No Man's Land, the Panhandle,
and a good share of Texas to get there, not
to mention the fact that you had to get by
the Comanche and God-only-knew-who-
else who were on the warpath right now in
that area! It was pure insanity. Me, I'd have
headed north to the Black Hills, where they
had a scarce population and a lot of hiding
places. But this wasn't a time to be ponder-
ing such things, so I stuck to trailing them.

They were good. I'll give them that. I'm a
fairly good tracker, but these fellows would
ride for a while, then hit a stream and follow it a ways before making tracks again. It
slowed me down, covering all the ground,
giving them maybe an hour's lead on me.
There were times I was tempted to head off
in the direction of a cloud of dust I saw on
the horizon, but the wind had come up, and
that made little dust devils common, so that
cloud was no help at all. Every once in a

while I'd look back, but there was no one coming from town. It must have been one hell of a fire they were putting out.

It was getting on toward dark and I was feeling hungry when I heard a horse behind me and saw Hard Luck Hank riding up as fast as he could.

"You the only one they could spare from town?" I asked. Somehow, Hank wasn't what I'd call my idea of a relief force. If you know what I mean.

"You should have been there, Guns!" he said, as out-of-breath as his mount. "There were horses all over the place and a big fire. They almost had it out when I left town."

"And you were the only one who had a horse to come join me?"

"Wel-l-l," he said reluctantly, "not really. Let's just say that while the others were out rounding up the horses that scattered . . . I borrowed this one."

"I see." It wasn't going to do any good to make a fuss over it now, so I let it go and told him to start gathering up some dead-wood for a fire. Besides, he'd brought a Sharps with him, and an extra gun, even just one, would be helpful in my mission. I could not hope that he hadn't stolen the buffalo gun to make the trip out here; in fact, I didn't ask him about it at all in order to to avoid learning more about his borrowing habits.

"Sis says she and Johnny want you to be in on their wedding," he said after I'd boiled some coffee. The way he was smiling made me wonder if he wasn't back to his prankish ways.

"That's what I heard. But I ain't gonna do it." I poured some coffee. "Told Johnny to check with you about standing up for him. I just ain't that keen on weddings."

"If you don't, she's really gonna be hurt, Guns. Sis really likes you, you know. Oh, she *loves* Johnny and all, but it's you she likes, Guns. In your own way you're special to her. That's why it ought to be you that serves as best man." He took another gulp of coffee before adding, "Besides, I can't. I'm gonna be leaving when we get back to Dodge."

"Leaving? Where you got to go to, boy?" That in itself would be an interesting find-out, for I'd never heard him mention any family, out here or back there.

"I don't know." He shrugged. "I'll just drift, I reckon. I've been pretty much of a bother to most everyone I've met out here. I'll find a little two-horse town . . . or maybe a way station where I won't get in that much trouble. Maybe."

I wasn't sure if he was serious or not, but if he was looking for sympathy, he was telling his troubles to the wrong person. Me, I had other things on my mind.

"At least you learned one thing out here, Hank, and that is that you make your own decisions and stand by them, good or bad."

He didn't say much to that, and we spent the rest of the night in silence. The next morning we were up early and on the trail even before daylight. I had a notion that if I played my hand right, I'd be able to catch up with those outlaws before the sun set on another day.

And I was right.

They'd run out of creeks to cross and left an easy trail to follow, probably because one of their horses looked like it'd come up lame, according to the tracks. It was early afternoon when I saw one of those dust devils — or was it trail dust? — and decided that since I now had a partner, I'd take a chance and check out my suspicions.

"Hank, you follow this trail," I said. "I'm heading for those foothills over there and see if our friends might not be making a quick cut for the southwest."

"But what if there's shooting?" he asked, sounding concerned.

"You just follow this trail. I can take care

196

of myself."

He didn't like what I'd said, but he'd learned by now not to argue with me and continued riding in silence as I took off toward the foothills, which got bigger and bigger as I neared them.

The trail dust had stayed constant, so I dug my heels into the horse, urging him on. Somehow I knew it was at least one of them I was chasing; knew it for sure when the dust disappeared behind the butte that was coming closer and closer into view. That wasn't any lame horse he was riding, so I had to catch up to him quick, or I'd lose him for sure, especially the way my own mount was panting now. Trouble was I'd begun to make an obsession out of capturing this killer, and it wasn't for the money that I wanted him anymore.

Distractions, innocent or planned, have probably killed more men than anything else I can think of, and the outlaw I was pursuing was purely distracting. I say that because I was so intent on catching him that I didn't see his partner coming at me from the side. I'd clean forgotten that all he had to do was cut across to the west and he'd be within rifle range of me, lame horse or no. I didn't know he was to my left front until his bullet hit me in the shoulder and I went tumbling off my horse, hearing the shot ring out as I fell.

I must have bruised my ribs when I landed, but I still had my Sharps clutched tight in my fist, not wanting to lose that for nothing. Whatever caliber he was using had stunned me and hurt like hell, but I was still breathing, and like I'd told that fellow, there was the mad factor. Landing on my keister wasn't something I was used to, and dammit, that didn't sit right, not at all.

By the time I got my senses back and was able to get to my feet, he was heading right at me, pointing a rifle in one hand and a pistol in the other.

"I'm coming to save you, Guns!" I heard Hank yell in the distance, and then his Sharps boomed and my attacker flew out of his saddle, his horse racing by me, empty. All of a sudden I gained a whole new respect for Hard Luck Hank as he mounted and rode to my side. He had a smile on his face that told me he must have known he had finally done something right. I was about to tell him I'd buy him a beer, when a third shot rang out and he fell from his horse.

It was the man I'd been after who'd done the shooting. He hadn't kept going after he'd gotten around that butte. He'd dismounted and made his way to near the top of it and had a clear shot at all of us. He was still standing there, reloading, likely thinking he could do me in, too, since there wasn't any cover.

I gave my horse the flat of my hand on its rump and got it out of the way, letting him see where I was. He was seven, maybe eight hundred yards away, and as good as he was with his rifle, I could easily die. I knew it, but I didn't care as I took a quick aim at him and squeezed the hair trigger on that Big Fifty of mine.

"Son of a bitch," I said, lowering the rifle and watching as the distant figure fell down the side of that butte, the clatter of his rifle echoing in the hills. Even if I'd only wounded him, the fall would have killed him. But that didn't even matters up, not by a long shot, for when I looked back at Hank, I knew he didn't have long to live. He was chest-shot in a place where it wouldn't do any good to have the best surgeon in the world, not a-tall.

"You saved my life, Hank," I said, kneeling down beside him.

"Just like you said, Guns," he choked, trying to smile. "I done what was expected of me." He grimaced again.

"That's right, Hank, and then some, too."

"She really is special, you know. . . ." He never finished it; but I figured I knew what it was he was trying to say.

There were hoofbeats in the distance to my rear, and I automatically found myself reloading just in case someone else had it in mind to use me for a target. But when the riders got closer, I took a deep breath and sighed, remembering that my left arm was on fire. Jim Hanrahan was the first one I recognized of the dozen or so men who were approaching. I stood up, feeling more than a mite dizzy trying to stay on my feet, but I managed.

"Ain't you just a wee bit late, fellas?" I asked, and fell forward as I passed out.

CHAPTER 16

Like everyone else, I've had nightmares at one time or another in my life, but never dreams that were as painful as those I had that night. Except it wasn't the dreams that was giving me all that pain. I figured that one out when I came to the next morning and just lay there in the predawn stillness knowing that the slug in me had been taken out. All I could see were the stars above me, and I had no urge to move about real quick to look at what was on the skyline, but I knew it couldn't be long before daylight. There was coffee boiling, and I heard the crackle a dying fire makes when it's being brought to life again.

"Pa always said life was one damn thing after another," I said to no one in particular.

"What's that?" a posse member asked, then said, "Guns, glad to see you coming 'round. I told 'em you was too big to die." The thought of dying brought to mind Hard

Luck Hank more than my own status among the living. After all, it wasn't the first time I'd been shot and probably wouldn't be the last the way my life was going of late, but then I reckon my time hadn't come yet. When I asked about Hank, the man said, "We buried him last night. Buried him deep, Guns. Ain't no wolves gonna get to that boy."

"If you think you can sit up now, I'll pour you some *real* coffee," a familiar gravelly voice said, and Fat Jack came into view.

"What the hell are you doing out here?" I asked as he gave me a hand getting into an upright position. "Who's taking care of the saloon?"

"Left Sis in charge, believe it or not," he said, pouring out some coffee and adding a slosh of liquid from a pocket flask he carried.

"Sis! But who's watching *her?*"

He smiled. "Who do you think?" I shouldn't even have asked the question, for as long as Sis was around, there'd be Colorado Johnny to look out for her, no matter what she was doing.

"Lordy, Jack, what did you put in this coffee!" I said when I took a healthy gulp and nearly choked on it. I'm used to hot coffee all right, but it was what was in this stuff that felt like it was taking the lining off the walls of my throat all the way down.

"Busthead, Aged in the Keg," he pronounced proudly, "two hundred proof. Want some more?"

"Not hardly! This stuff tastes like it'll kill you from the inside." I shivered as the effect of the whiskey, or whatever it was, took hold in my empty stomach.

"That may be, pard, but I wouldn't complain too awful hard if I was you. You may think it'll kill you from the inside, but it saved you from the outside last night!"

"Saved me?"

"Why, sure." He gave me a dumbfounded look, as if I should know exactly what he was talking about, since I'd been present when it took place. "Fellas didn't have nothing to sterilize your wound with, so I donated some of my Busthead."

"That must've been the pain I was feeling," I mumbled.

"Pardon?"

"Nothing, Jack. Nothing."

I had him dilute my cup with more coffee before I attempted to drink any more of it. Just the right dosage of this home brew of Jack's and I figured I'd have my system cleaned out in an hour, be blind by noon and ready for the coffin by sunset. And the undertaker wouldn't even need any embalming fluid!! I felt a bit better about it when someone threw some bacon into a pan and took to frying it, knowing there'd be something inside me to absorb all of this poison.

"You know, Guns, I been dealing in liquor for the better part of a decade now," Jack said when the food was ready and the camp was coming to life. "Been dealing with drunks for about that long, too, I'd say. Found me out more secrets than the town gossip ever will." He chuckled. "Poor fella's got a problem, though, you see."

"What's that?"

"Once they get down past a certain part of the bottle, they git to talking, and it's the unvarnished truth that comes out. Let you know what they really think of the reverend and the mayor and their partner or wife, who they think is cheating on them."

"Know what you mean," I said, and finished my coffee. There's something about a decent meal and good hot coffee that brings a wounded man back to life some, and as sore as my arm was feeling, I had a renewed sense of being about me. At least I wouldn't be flat on my back for a week like some people might.

"Did you know that delirious folks do the

same thing?" He said it in a low voice, looking at me out of the corner of his eye.

"What are you getting at, Jack?"

"Truth of the matter is that last night when that slug was being taken out of you, why, you gave us a whole account of what went on here . . . how you and Hank got shot up and all.

"Later, when most of them were out digging Hank's grave, I sat watch over you and heard a whole nother story. Something about a diamond being stolen and some other ramblings." He squinted at me the way you do when you're trying to make out someone from a distance. "Now, that wouldn't be the one old Asa hired you to find, would it? 'Cause something tells me there's a lot that ain't right about this whole situation."

It was getting so I was confiding in more people than I cared to, more than I'd planned on, for certain. But you don't always get your druthers in this world. It's the way of things. So here I was, spinning my tale to Fat Jack. But at least I could trust him.

"Then have a seat, Jack, and I'll enlighten you."

I don't know where they got it, but someone

had placed a small flat piece of wood on the pile of stones that stood as Hank's grave marker. I knew the wolves and other animals would scatter the stones and the wood would blow away or get dragged away in time. Looking at it made me wonder just how much was permanent in this land, hell, in this *world.*

"Tough, ain't it?" Jack said as the others led their horses away from camp, leaving the bartender and me standing there by Hank's grave.

"Losing a friend? Yeah." It felt odd to stand there calling a man a friend only after he'd died saving my life. Somehow I got the feeling that if Hank could speak just then, he'd ask me if I wasn't being just a mite two-faced, and I couldn't deny it.

"There's that," Jack said, "but it wasn't what I was thinking about." Eyeing that grave, he shook his head. "Every time I see one of these, it reminds me how people go through life."

"How's that, Jack?"

"Using every excuse they got to cheat death." He sloshed on his hat. "Always turns out the same, though."

Hanrahan and his men had found the bank's money on the dead men after our shoot-out and were taking care to get it back to the town safely. Me, I was feeling right tender on one side and wasn't in any hurry to open up the wound. It was a .44-40 that had hit me and had stopped in the fleshy part of my arm without breaking any bones or ricocheting inside the way a bullet can do if it strikes the right place. I reckon there was just more of me to get through. When Hanrahan and his men let it be known that they had businesses to tend back in town and that they had to be getting on back to them, I told them not to worry, that I could take care of myself. That was when Fat Jack volunteered to ride along with me just in case I needed any further doctoring.

"You must have a lot of faith in Sis to let her take care of your saloon that long."

"Total faith." He smiled. "She's served enough drinks to know the prices by heart, and she won't water down the liquor. One thing you got to admit about my place, Guns. Some of what I serve might be home brew, but there ain't a bit of it that's ever been watered down. No, sir." He said it with a measure of pride, as much as you'd find in any professional man with a fancy diploma from back East.

"What if someone tries to take advantage of her? She does look a bit on the frail side, you know."

"Not a chance," Jack said, smiling again. "That Colorado Johnny, that boy's gonna make something of himself, you watch. And moon-eyed as she is over him . . . well, hoss, he ain't gonna let nothing happen to Sis. Besides, those fellas in Dodge know what'll happen to 'em if they do touch her."

That seemed to be the last word on any doubts Fat Jack may have had on the safety of his business, and well it should be. No man in his right mind would ever do harm to a woman in public or private in town, for it would be hard to explain how the woman came about any physical abuse if it was done in private, and if he threatened or hit a woman in public in front of witnesses, well, as Pa would put it, he was gone beaver. Women were too precious a commodity on the frontier not to be held in high regard by the male community. I'd heard stories of instances in which a man had admitted to harming a woman and been hung on the spot with no regrets or guilt felt by those who had lynched him. And if anyone tried anything with Sis while Colorado Johnny was around . . . like I said, that boy could snake that Colt's out of his holster like no one I'd ever seen before.

I'd ridden a good forty miles before I'd caught up with the bank robbers. A fast, hard ride would get us back to Dodge in a day or so, but I was content to ride ten or fifteen miles a day instead and be in better shape for it than to risk reopening my wound. Bleeding to death never did hold much attraction for me as a way to end my life. So Fat Jack and I took our time and let the horses do most of the work.

I did some piecing together that first day, recalling some things that had seemed strange when they happened but all of a sudden made a hell of a lot of sense. For instance, that fight I'd had with Lance Carver two or three months back. It had happened on the same day the jewelry store was robbed; in fact, it had been at nearly the same time the store was robbed. Maybe it was coincidence, but the more I thought about it, the more I was convinced that it hadn't been. Lance Carver was big and mean and had gained a reputation for being willing to fight at the drop of a hat, but he'd stayed pretty much to himself, because besides being big and mean, he was also on the far side of what you'd call ugly and he knew no woman would have him. The only reason nothing had been done to Carver after that fight was probably because the town had the same impression that I had, that Hard Luck Hank had set the whole thing up as a joke at my expense. Now I realized that the whole incident *had* been staged for my benefit, and perhaps even the town's, but by someone other than Hank.

And it hadn't been a joke.

The outcome had stuck me with a diamond I didn't particularly want but that was growing in popularity the longer I had it. After my run-in with those two plug uglies in the alley and my own place had been torn to bits, I had no doubts at all that it was the diamond they were after. In fact, I would have put money of the fact that Carver had been a part of the gang who'd held up the store, the diamond being the only reason he had signed up with Charlie Myers to go down to Adobe Walls. Word had gotten around that I was ramrodding the outfit, so Carver signed on. I should have known it then, for as convincing as he was to Myers, the truth was that Lance Carver had been a bit like me in one respect. He'd wanted to make as much money for as little work as I did. It's just that Carver had a reputation for going about it in an other-than-honest manner. He'd come along to keep an eye on me, knowing that I either had the diamond on me or had hidden it someplace safe. Then he must have followed me back to Dodge when I'd returned for supplies with Colorado Johnny and Hard Luck Hank, and he'd found his opportunity to jump me at the general store. As mean as he was, Carver probably had it in mind to shoot off my fingers and toes until I told him the location of the diamond. Either that or the need for revenge had taken over his mind and he wanted to get rid of me in the worst way, diamond or no diamond. But then the Carvers of this world are like that.

That night we camped near a grove of trees that was located next to a creek. The water was clear and the horses found some forage, so we decided it would do. Fat Jack said he had some Arbuckles, if I had a pot to boil it in, and we had coffee along with a prairie chicken Jack had shot. By the time we were through eating, we wished it had been two chickens he'd shot, for we both had good appetites. But the coffee made up for it, being hot, strong, and black. Fact is, sometimes I think a body could go a whole day on one pot of that coffee, as thick as it got in the making.

Sometimes I wonder if I think too much. I reckon it's fine to turn something over in your mind until you figure it out; yes, it is. On the other hand, it can be downright distracting if you aren't careful of how far you carry it. Maybe if I'd been paying more attention to the trail and the country around me that day, I wouldn't have come as close to dying as I did that night. Like I said, sometimes I wonder if I think too much.

He was either a bad shot or just giving us a warning when the rifle boomed in the near darkness and sent my coffeepot flying off the fire. Whichever it was, I'd had my fill of being shot at and dropped my cup and rolled to the side into the shadows, the same as Fat Jack did. As usual, my Sharps wasn't far away and I had it in my hands within a matter of seconds. I wasn't sure if Fat Jack would stay where he was or move to the outside of the camp perimeter the way I was doing, but it didn't really matter, for I knew the man could take care of himself. In a tight spot Jack could serve up lead as well as he did his home brew, be it with a pistol or rifle. Me, I was going on the hunt. I went toward what sounded like the skittishness of other horses besides our own, which was coming from the direction the shot had been fired from.

The light from the part of the moon that was out helped, but my eyes were adjusted to the dark, so I'd have gotten him anyway. One shadowy figure had just mounted up and was tearing hell-for-leather out of there, and I took a bead on the other one, who was about to climb onto his horse.

"Mister!" I yelled as I took aim. Like I figured he would, he panicked and turned, going for his side gun as he did. He was dead in my sights when I pulled the trigger and dead permanently as the bullet passed through him and into his saddle, scaring off his mount as he fell to the ground.

"The other one's gone, Guns," Jack said, coming out of the trees. "Saddle up; there might be enough light for us to go after him."

With the toe of my boot, I turned the dead man over onto his back. He had a look of shock on his face, and hatchet-like features I had seen before some time back. It had been a dimly lit alley where I'd seen that face before as he and his partner had tried to jump me. I'd gotten away that time by firing off that Sharps of mine. This time the buffalo gun had done more than simply scare them.

"No need, Jack. Might as well get some sleep."

"But what about —"

"Ain't gonna matter if you follow the trail tonight or tomorrow, Jack," I said, looking down at my ruined coffeepot as we returned to the campfire. "I'd bet money it'll wind up in Dodge City."

CHAPTER 17

I was cautious for the next day and a half that it took us to get back to Dodge. Not overly cautious, just cautious. But you'd have been acting the same way if someone had potshotted you, friend; yes, I do believe you would. Still, I found a bit of time to try to refit the pieces of the puzzle that had me thoroughly confused now.

The only reason anyone could have for killing me was in connection with that stolen diamond, and I was beginning to wish I'd never seen the damn thing in the first place. When the bank was robbed and Turner claimed the two who'd pulled the robbery were the same ones who'd stolen his merchandise, I'd thought that was the end of it. Especially after Hard Luck Hank and I had tracked them down and killed them, recovering the bank money. Odds were that they had hidden the jewels some-place or had gotten rid of them and decided to stretch their luck a second time in the same town. But just like Hank's, their luck had run out.

Now I had almost been killed by the birds who had also tried to do me in a few months back. Where did they fit in? It was a near certainty that Carver had hired them to jump me in the alley that night, but now I found myself wondering if they, too, hadn't been connected with the jewelry robbery and maybe even the bank robbery. How big was this gang?

Or was I simply someone who people thought would make a good target for some shooting practice? The whole problem just seemed to get more complicated the more I thought about it, so I settled on trying to find the answers to the two most important questions in my mind: Who was trying to kill me and, above all, *why?*

We got some strange looks, Jack and I, riding into Dodge with that body draped over the extra horse like it was. Most folks were more used to seeing supplies on the backs of animals that were led into town than dead bodies, I reckon. But that's what civilization does to people, makes them skittish about death. A newborn colt's the same way about people when it comes into this world, but it gets over that feeling. Town folk, well, it just seems that the more civilized they get, the more skittish they stay. I reined in in front of the marshal's office while Fat Jack headed for his saloon, which was still standing. Yes, Sis had apparently made a good bartender.

"Not you again," the marshal groaned as I dismounted. Sometimes a person gets a picture of a man in his head and tends to label him if he disrupts that person's life and duties. This lawman, well, he'd had to let me go after Johnny and I killed Carver, but you can bet he just *knew* I was a born troublemaker. All of which was confirmed when he saw the dead man, and he shook his head in disbelief.

"A man don't always get his druthers, Marshal," I said. "But look on the bright side. I brought you some company. And by the way," I added, "if he's got a price on his head, I'll take it."

That didn't make the lawman any more friendly toward me.

"You're pretty sly, ain't you, mister? You ride into town claiming to be a buffalo hunter, and —"

"Anything wrong with that?" I asked, feeling my fist ball up like it did sometimes.

"Just one thing, Hooker. I ain't seen you with a buffalo hide yet this season, and you

216

ain't done nothing but show me dead bodies since you turned up in this town. Ask me, you're more of a bounty hunter than a buffalo hunter. What I oughtta do is —"

"What you *oughtta do* is listen to my side of the story before you start throwing threats and your weight around." If I sounded like I was tired of taking guff from people, it's because I was, and I swear that if he hadn't been a lawman, I'd have shoved that Big Fifty square into his gut and asked him what he thought about dying. As it was, I just gave him my meanest look and let the tone of my voice convey the rest to him. "That sonofabitch tried to kill me, marshal, but he did a damn poor job of it. Now if you want to keep from calling me a liar and starting your own fandango with me, go on across the street and ask Fat Jack about how it happened. He was with me and he'll verify it.

"As for your opinion about just what I am . . . well, marshal, you can do one of two things with that as far as I'm concerned. You can keep it to yourself" — I paused here, giving him a hard look that said I was fed up with his accusations — "or you can take off your badge and step out in the street. Don't make much difference to me, but if I was you, I'd take the first choice.

"And if you were thinking that you oughtta throw me out of town . . . I wouldn't do it. There's a *federal* marshal who's a good friend of mine a few towns over, and I'll guarantee you that if politics was how you got elected to this position, you'll never hold it again. What you want to do, mister, is understand one thing: I never set out to kill a man in my lifetime that didn't try to do the same damn thing to me *first.* You got any doubts about that, you ask around." I took my reins and got up into the saddle, grimacing as I leaned into my wounded left shoulder to do so; it was still sore as hell and needed some healing time.

"Jim Hanrahan brought in a couple more bodies a few days back, I reckon, from that bank robbery," I said. "Hard Luck Hank and I pegged 'em, so if they had any wanted money on their heads, I'll take it, too. Hank must have had a family somewhere. Now, if you'll excuse me, marshal, I've got to get fixed up and get something to eat."

He didn't say much as I left, but the look about him was a bothersome one, which meant he'd check out what I'd told him just to make sure it was on the level. And that was fine with me, for I had nothing to hide.

The town doctor wasn't too busy, and he checked and rebandaged my wound, administering a solution that wasn't nearly as painful as the home brew Fat Jack had used in getting the bullet out. He said that if I was smart, I'd stay off my feet, get some rest, and build my strength back up. I'd been drinking a lot of water on the way back into town, which the doctor said was good, since it was needed to help replace the blood I'd lost. He had a whole headful of knowledge about patch-up work, this doctor, but from the row of thick medical books perched atop his desk, I reckon that was to be expected.

My next stop was the eatery so I could bring my stomach up to date on what decently prepared food really tasted like. I'd finished my beefsteak and was working on a piece of apple pie when the marshal walked in and made himself comfortable at my table, ordering a cup of coffee before he sat down.

"Better be careful, marshal," I said. "Folks see you sitting at the same table as me, you might get your reputation tarnished."

"I'll bet you're a good grudge fighter," he said.

"Only when I have cause to be."

"Well, maybe you'll want to forget about grudges and do some listening for a change." I'd given him a dose of his own medicine, and he plainly didn't like it.

"What for? I thought you had me all figured out."

"I did some asking around." He pushed his hat back and took a sip of his coffee, making himself right at home. "Charlie Myers and a few others said you did real good at that Adobe Walls bust-up. And Jack confirmed your story about Taylor. . . . That's the name of the dead man you brought in."

"That's interesting." I said it casually as if it meant nothing at all, but I knew that I could use the money, *if* he was a wanted man, and the information the marshal might have on him *if* he was willing to share it. As cool as I played it, the marshal must have read my eyes.

"There was two hundred dollars on his head. I just sent a wire out for the money. Ought to be here in a couple of days."

"That'll be nice. I'm about broke anyway."

It was cat and mouse that we were playing, each one of us being real casual about all of this but both knowing that we were each going to need information that the other had eventually. It was all a matter of who was going to do the asking first, and it turned out that the lawman was a bit more anxious than I was.

"Look, Hooker, I think it's about time we started helping one another out instead of butting heads." When I said nothing, he added, "Fat Jack says you've got some right interesting ideas about these robberies we've had of late. Now, if that's right, I'd appreciate you letting me in on it, 'cause that's more my territory than yours. I'm working on the identity of those two Hanrahan brought in, and if they have a reward on either of them, I'll make sure you get it, too."

"Are you going to stop treating me like some down-and-out killer, then?"

The Marshal shrugged. "Man's entitled to a mistake every now and then. Besides, there's more than enough riff-raff, who pass through this town that I'd just as soon kept moving on. The ones who are handier than most with a gun, well, I tend to help 'em along."

The waiter refilled our cups, and I found myself suddenly curious about a number of things concerning the robbers.

"I wonder if that fella I brought in might have had himself a partner of sorts."

"Could be, Hooker," the lawman replied. "According to my poster, he was known to work once in a while with a tall, lanky fella on his jobs. Think you might know the man?"

I had a hunch that he was the one who had gotten away before I'd nailed his friend, and I said as much to the marshal.

"That's fine, but how is it you figure you can link him and his partner up with the jewelry robbery?"

"I don't know, marshal," I said, and went on to explain that most of the ideas I had were pure speculation but that I thought there had to be a connection between Lance Carver and the four men we'd been talking about. "There isn't a helluva lot of it that makes any sense, yet they all seem to be connected to this business one way or another."

For an instant it crossed my mind that the description the marshal had just given fit Colorado Johnny right down to the button, but I dismissed the thought. Besides, the boy had proven he was a crack shot and could hit what he aimed at. No, it couldn't be Johnny. Fact is, it was about then that Johnny came strolling through the door of the eatery and gave a quick scan of the place before seeing me.

"Jack said I'd likely find you over here," he said, making himself as at home at my table as the lawman had. He smiled as he said, "Got word back on that telegram you told me to send the other day. Real interesting word."

"Telegram? Word? What are you talking about, boy?" the lawman asked in pure puzzlement.

"Sounds like I was right, Johnny. Why don't you enlighten our friend here."

"Yes, son, why don't you do that?"

"Well, sir, I did some checking, like Guns wanted me to, and I found out a whole lot. Yes, sir, a *whole* lot. Our Mister Asa Turner was a once-upon-a-time clerk in a fancy jewelry store back in Saint Louis. He decided to come out West and convinced the owner he could make a fortune selling some of that jewelry here in Dodge."

"What's so unusual about that?" the lawman asked. "There must be a hundred, hell, a thousand men who've done the same thing."

"With forty thousand dollars of their boss's stock?"

"Well, maybe not that much." The marshal's sentence trailed off.

"I didn't think so." Johnny had picked up the habit of pushing his hat back on his head when he got into a good story, something I caught myself doing once in a while. "What he didn't seem to count on, I reckon, is the fact that Dodge ain't much more'n a stop-off place for the stage and an entertainment spot for the buffalo hunters once a year and the soldiers at Fort Dodge the rest of the time, and they spend most of their money on liquor, cards, and women."

"So you're saying that Asa Turner wasn't making much of a profit here in Dodge."

"Exactly," Johnny said. He had the marshal hooked now, so badly that the lawman didn't even notice the refill he'd gotten on his coffee. I think Johnny was just as excited to be telling the story.

"I wonder why he'd pick a place like Dodge City, though," the marshal said, obviously thinking out loud.

"Only thing I can figure is that Fat Jack is his brother-in-law," I said, throwing in my own two cents worth. "Turner married Jack's sister some time back, and she died sudden. I reckon if you look at it from the right angle, that'd give him an excuse for coming to Dodge before going anywhere else. Jack would be able to get him set up and started."

"You know, Hooker, you might have more brains than people give you credit for," the marshal said, but all the time I could see the wheels turning in his mind as he started putting the puzzle together in his own way.

"I know who most of the people are in this town who have the money. Maybe I'll do some checking with them to see if they've bought anything from Turner. But beyond that, I've got to have something concrete, something solid to get the man on, *if* he's our man."

"In that case, marshal, I'll throw you an ace in the hole." A smile came to Johnny's face now, for it was this piece of information he'd been wanting to pass on, at least by the look of him. He pulled out his pistol and laid it on the table.

"This Colt's of mine and Gun's Sharps are what we use to protect ourselves out here." He smiled at me when he added, "Sort of insurance against catching up with my mother and father too soon."

"Sometimes not even that works," the older man said. "But what's that got to do with what we were talking about?"

"Fella I lived with in my younger days — Mister Odom was his name — he knew all sorts of things about life. Me, I had the good sense to listen to him when he was talking."

"Go on."

"Well, marshal, one of the things I remember him telling me about was insurance." The boy stopped, stared at his cup, remembering better days and better times, and a smile came to his face again. "Mister Odom, he didn't think too much of insurance companies. Figure they were made for people who were playing both ends against the middle, folks who were trying to buy a memory with money after they'd died."

"Son, if all you want to do is reminisce, you can wait until the night man comes on duty and sit up until dawn talking to him." It was plain to see that the lawman was getting impatient. "Now, you were saying something about an ace in the hole, so why don't you deal it."

"Oh, yeah. What I was getting at, sir, is that folks back East have got their own way of protecting themselves. Somebody steals something from you or me, we'll take out after him with a horse and gun and track him until we get it back. Those easterners, well, it seems they don't much care if they get back what was stolen or not, because if they got it insured, why, they can get their money back on it anyway.

"What I'm getting at is that I did some checking and found out that Asa Turner had a whole passel of insurance on those jewels that were stolen from him." From the way Johnny looked as he finished his story, I could tell he was expecting a pat on the back from our local lawman, but he didn't get it.

"If that's your kicker, son, then it's as thin as the rest of the evidence we've got on Mister Turner. Hell, even if he did have insurance on those gems, he'd only get their market value, and if that was forty thousand dollars, it would seem to me that he'd still have his old boss fella in Saint Louis to pay back. And if he didn't do that, why, he'd be as wanted as the James boys." He shook his head. "Sorry, son, it just won't wash."

"It would if he planned to collect on the insurance money *and* recovered the jewels, then stayed in business as if nothing out of the ordinary had happened," I said.

The marshal gave me a curious look then, the wheels turning again in his mind as he began to see what I was getting at.

"In other words —"

I nodded. "Asa Turner set up this whole robbery bit. In fact, I'm wondering if he might not have engineered the bank holdup, too."

CHAPTER 18

There was no way I could prove that Asa Turner was behind any of the robberies unless I could get him to admit it, and that seemed an unlikely prospect. All I had was his word on it that the two who had robbed the bank were the same ones who had robbed him. I didn't even know if anyone had thought to ask him to identify the bodies when they'd been brought back to town along with the money. It probably wouldn't have mattered to most folks as long as they got their deposits back in the bank safely. Still, there was something about that whole robbery that was bothering me, had bothered me from the start. Then things began falling into place as much for me as they had for the marshal, and I decided to do some checking of my own.

The lawman finally identified himself as Ira Stone, marshal of Dodge City. I figured that since he knew who we were, we might as well know the same about him if we were going to be working together . . . in a sense, that is. When we finished the talk, Stone said he was going to follow up on checking with some of those rich folks in town to see if any had indeed bought jewelry from Turner or had anything to do with him at all. He was a real cautious man, that marshal. He'd want a pat hand before he was going to do any betting and said he'd have most of the information he needed in an hour or so, if I cared to meet him at Turner's store.

The meal had done me some good, the hour I'd sat in the eatery's having given me a little of the rest the doctor had recommended. Not that I felt like taking on the whole world, you understand, for my shoulder was still aching. But the interest I'd taken in what had happened to Asa Turner had made dealing with that pain a mite easier now. Or maybe it was the thought in the back of my mind that if we didn't get this thing settled and soon, someone else might be using me for a target, and I'd had my fill of being shot at that spring!

One of the things that still bothered me was the description Marshal Stone had given of the partner that Taylor man worked with. Being tall and thin could fit any one of a hundred different men in town, but I kept running into people and things that just didn't fit where they were supposed to — and it was unsettling to say the least. So I headed for Fat Jack's.

"Hi, Guns!" I heard Sis say before I could adjust my eyes to the darkness. In a way it was sort of a shock, yet it was pleasing to hear her say it. When she'd had that crush on me, she wouldn't call me anything but Matt, but hearing her say my nickname now gave me an easy feeling about being around her. At least I wouldn't have to worry about her throwing herself at me whenever I came into view anymore.

"Kept her on, did you?" I asked Jack as he set a beer down before me.

"I had to!" he said in a state of disbelief. Then, leaning closer, he lowered his voice as if taking me into his confidence. "Would you believe that the whole bunch of them said they'd leave if I didn't let her finish out the day!" He gave a furtive glance at the customers in the room. "Patrons, my ass! Said I was too ugly to serve 'em! *Ugly!* Now, I ask you, Guns, do I look ugly?"

Jack knew he was no catch when it came to finding a lady friend, which, when you think of it, may be why he'd never thought much of the institution of marriage. I smiled when I replied, "If I tell you the truth, you'll never serve me again."

"Patrons!" he grumbled to himself, and walked off.

I finished my beer and waited for Sis to catch up in her waitress duties before asking her any questions, for it was her I wanted to talk to more than Jack. When she set a fresh beer before me, I asked how things had gone while Jack was away.

"Oh, it was wonderful, Guns," she said with that aura a woman has about her when she gets love-struck. "Having Johnny around was *wonderful.*"

I smiled. "I meant how'd you like actually running a bar by yourself?"

"Oh." She shrugged nonchalantly. "It was all right, I guess."

"I gather you were paying a good deal of attention to Johnny."

"Yeah," she replied dreamily.

"Didn't get any trouble at all, huh?"

"Only once, but Chuck over there gave me a hand." She pointed to an older man I had seen at the bar before, a regular of Fat Jack's.

I laughed, trying to sound as casual as possible. "You mean there was something our Colorado Johnny couldn't handle by himself?"

"Of course not!" Only a woman as in love

as Sis was could get so indignant at a moment's notice, but I reckon they tend to act that way when anything about their man comes into question. "That was the day Johnny wasn't here, so Chuck helped out running the place."

"Oh?"

"Yes, Johnny said he had some business to take care of." She began polishing a glass just like a professional barkeep. "Boy, it sure must've taken some doing, cause he was gone all day and didn't ride in until late the next afternoon."

"I'll bet it did," I said, the humor draining out of me at the thought of how wrong I had been. Riding hell-for-leather both ways would have given Colorado Johnny enough time to arrive at our campsite the night we had been ambushed and make it back to town just about the time Sis was saying he did. A shiver ran down my spine as I found myself wondering how I would come out against the boy I had treated damn near like a son. Damn it, it happened to me every time I got to trusting someone. No sooner did I get to liking them than they turned out to be entirely different from who they'd made themselves out to be. What made it worse was the knowledge that Johnny was out with the marshal now, and if it was

Johnny who'd been in cahoots with that Taylor fellow, well, I had a feeling I wouldn't be finding the local law showing up at Asa Turner's when he'd said he would.

"You screw up that face much more, Guns, and you'll break my mirror if you look in it." Fat Jack was chiding me but doing it cautiously.

"You ever loan any money to your brother-in-law while he was here in Dodge?"

"Well, now, do you really think you ought to —"

I slammed the flat of my hand on the bar, the surface visibly moving some. Damn it, there wasn't nothing that had panned out that spring!

"Just answer me." I said it slow and low, and Fat Jack knew me well enough to realize that I had a slow burn and that if he didn't want his place broken up, he'd best not argue with me in this condition.

"Well . . . yeah. He had to get started up and all. Say, just what are you getting at?"

I drank the rest of the beer, setting the glass down on the bar gently. I smiled as best I could, but happy wasn't what I was feeling, and Jack knew that, too.

"You remember all that complaining you used to do about your relatives, Jack?"

"Yeah, why?"

"Well, I've got a new line you can add to your list."

"Oh? And what would that be?" The way he said it I knew he had reached his level of tolerance of me.

"In-laws are outlaws." I grabbed up the Big Fifty and was about to leave, when he grabbed hold of my arm real firm-like.

"What are you saying, Guns?"

"Asa Turner set up the whole bunch of robberies this town's had the past few months. I can't prove it yet, but as soon as I get down to his store, I'm gonna make a real believer out of him. Yes, sir, a real believer."

You never can tell about kinfolk. Most that are related to you by blood you will generally go out and defend when they get between a rock and a hard spot. As for in-laws . . . well, that can go either way. When Jack's hand moved below the bar, he was facing my Sharps when he brought the scattergun up in it. I had the rifle nestled in the crook of my arm and was looking at him over my left shoulder.

"You wasn't in with him, was you, Jack?"

He had the most confused look about him that I'd ever seen, and he was aiming it right at me as he set the gun on the bar. "What's gotten into you, Guns? Two days ago you

234

were confiding in me, and now you're acting like *I'm* the guy who's out for your blood! I thought you knew me better than that, Guns, I really did. And I thought I knew you better than that, too, but I guess I didn't." His face clouded up, and there was trouble in his voice. "Don't let them wings bat your keister too hard on the way out."

I didn't.

Sometimes you walk with a purposeful stride and it's force of habit and you don't notice it. Other times you do the same and you make sure everyone knows it. And that's how I was swaggering down the boardwalk when I headed for Turner's place. Some women gave me strange looks as they got out of my way. Others saw me coming and ducked into doorways before I reached them. But none of them tried to stop me, not even to converse about how rude they likely thought I was acting.

There were a lot of maybes going through my mind then. Maybe Asa Turner was as pure as the driven snow, and I was all wrong. Maybe Marshal Stone wouldn't show up at Turner's, but Colorado Johnny would. Maybe Jack was in on it with his brother-in-law. Maybe not. But I was tired and mad and I really didn't care. It's just one of those points that you reach that tears the blanket and there isn't anything that'll change it. Unless it's getting it all off your chest, and I surely aimed to do that. Yes, sir.

If Colorado Johnny or Marshal Stone was going to meet me at Turner's store, they hadn't arrived yet when I walked in. And in a way it was fine with me, for as cautious as the lawman was I didn't think he'd approve of the way I was going to find out the truth about Asa Turner. The store was empty; Asa Turner stood sternly behind the counter.

"I assume you've come to keep your part of the bargain and return the diamond," he said, no nonsense about him.

"Well, now, I'll tell you, Mister Turner. I never did get a chance to check those bank robbers for it. You see, one of 'em shot me before they both got done in. But I take a fair amount of killing. Or didn't you count on that?" Something I said threw him off, and of a sudden he was sounding right surprised. Either that or he was a good actor.

"I don't know what you're talking about." This fellow was about as changeable as the weather in some parts of the country I'd been in, severe one minute and mild the next.

"That so? Well, I think you're a *liar,* Turner." You call a man a liar in this part of the

236

country and you'd better be dead right, or you'd likely wind up dead. Hell, you could wind up that way anyway. It was as harsh a word as horse thief or cattle rustler, but I had a suspicion about these back-East types and I was right. They were better at politicking than anything else and would put up with being called damn near anything in the book so long as they could get your money. And Asa Turner wasn't any different, except that what he wanted from me was a diamond he knew I had.

"I can't say as I blame him, Mister Turner." I spotted Ira Stone out of the corner of my eye, entering the store to take a position next to me. "Sorry I was late, Hooker, but that Johnny is right inquisitive."

"Where is he now?" I was more than a bit curious.

"Said he was going to see that girl of his; Sis, is it?"

"Yeah, that's the one."

"Said he figured you and me could take care of Mister Turner without any problem." Another shiver went down my spine just knowing that Colorado Johnny was nowhere in sight. He had either totally lost interest in the whole mess — a fact that I found hard to believe — or he was planning on being a part of the problem itself. That was what gave me the chills.

"You know, that boy was right, Hooker," the marshal said. "There ain't been anyone with money in here for some time."

"That's preposterous!" the storekeeper blurted out.

"That'd be another lie, Turner," I said, this time with a smile of satisfaction, for that back-east accent suddenly fit another piece of the puzzle into place.

"You know, Stone, Hard Luck Hank was always reading those dime novels. I kept telling him they were trash, but he read 'em anyway," I remarked to the marshal.

"So?"

"One thing's been bothering me from the start of this business, that is that a lot of it seemed so much like it came out of a dime novel."

"What are you getting at?" Marshal Stone asked, his curiosity aroused now.

"This man hired me to find his jewelry, in particular a diamond he was interested in. Places I've been, if a man lost something of value and was willing to pay five hundred dollars to get it back, he'd let the whole town know about it, not just one lone man. You ask me, marshal, I'd say Turner was figuring I had his diamond and was willing to take a chance that I was greedy enough to ride out of town for one night, make myself a campfire, and ride back in, fork over the jewel, and collect my money and be done with it. Or he'd have someone follow me, kill me, and get his diamond back that way.

"Then there was the bank robbery. At first I couldn't place it, but something struck me as strange about it. Then this morning I remembered what it was. Turner here had brought me some shells over to the saloon when the bank was robbed. That's when he recognized the robbers as being the same ones who'd stolen his jewelry."

"Nothing wrong with that." Marshal Stone shrugged.

"Marshal, he identified them from the *back*," I said. "They had no particular markings on their horses; they wore slickers and were only of average height from what I could see. That description covers half of Kansas. If you ask me, he knew who they were and what they were doing. And it happened real conveniently, come to think of it — on a day when you were out of town. And it was *me* he got to go after the men."

"I see," the lawman said. "And no one else could go because of the fire in the livery."

"I'm betting there was someone he hired to set that fire at just the right time, too."

Asa Turner was sweating now as I guessed my way closer to what must have been the truth. Or maybe he simply couldn't believe how accurately I had put the story together. "This ain't like back East, you know," I said, addressing Turner now. "Rob a town's bank, take their money, why, you're liable to get *hung* for that out here." One way or another I was going to break him, and if a nudge toward the gallows was enough to bring him that much closer to confessing, then so be it.

"He's right," Stone said.

"These greenhorns from back East don't know a helluva lot about how life really is out here," I continued. "Closest they come is that trash in those dime novels. Turner here's likely enough of a crook to deal the likes of Carver in on his thievery. And high-handed as Turner tends to be, I'd say he even told Carver how he wanted that fight in the Long Branch staged. You remember that, don't you, Turner? The one that took place the *same* day and the *same* time as your store here got robbed." It was Asa Turner I had my eye on, but it was Ira Stone I was talking to now. "He might have had a robbery in this store, marshal, but I'm betting he was part of it. And as stingy as he is, you can bet those jewels ain't too far from

240

here either.

"Maybe it was Hard Luck Hank's bad luck that rubbed off on me that day and got me in the middle of all of this, but my saddlebags got fooled with just after the store got robbed. I bet Turner thinks that this diamond he's so fired up about finding might have been put in my reach then and that I know where it is now."

"*Do* you know where this diamond is?" Stone asked.

I glanced at the marshal, then at Turner, as I smiled and said, "Beats the hell outta me."

Turner had known I had it all along; he just didn't know where I had it. But I reckon every man has his weaknesses, and Asa Turner couldn't stand to go any longer without knowing where that precious stone of his was. It was his need to know that broke him.

"No! That can't be!" he was suddenly blurting out like a madman. His arm shot out, pointing past the marshal, his eyes bulging as he said, "He said you had it! He —"

"Shut up, Turner!" was the command that came from the store entrance, and it was enough to silence the storekeeper. The marshal turned as quick as I did, but I took a couple steps to the rear first, stepping on a floorboard that tended to squeak, hoping no one would notice as I brought the Sharps to full cock.

I'd only figured on one more partner in this crime, but like I said, people that had something to do with all of this were coming out of the woodwork every time I turned around. There were three of them standing there, one of whom moved off to my right and placed himself in front of that plate glass window that was the showcase for the store. He was tall and thin, all right, but an older man who, by the look of him, had been around awhile. Was this the one who'd partnered with Taylor, the one Marshal Stone had mentioned? Or was he connected with Colorado Johnny, who still had some explaining to do? The thin man had drawn a pistol, just like the other two.

I recognized that pair as the ones who'd come at me in the eatery after I'd returned from Adobe Walls, the ones who had goaded me into a fight. The difference was that they didn't look at all citified now; instead, they were wearing range clothes. But then you can't do much to hide ugly on some folks, and these two were that.

"You do too much talking," the tall, thin one said to Asa Turner before glaring at me.

"He's got that diamond all right, and he's going to hand it over or tell us where it is before we're through with him. Now, what's it gonna be, Hooker? Carver told me you had the stone."

Now, hoss, being outnumbered three to two isn't anything close to my view of fair odds, especially when you consider that I only had one shot with my Big Fifty and that the lawman next to me didn't show any promise as being another John Wesley Hardin with a gun. I didn't have a clear view of Asa Turner either and didn't know if he had pulled out a gun from beneath the counter or not. I'd have to count on him being too damn scared to do such a thing. Trouble was they had the drop on us, and that meant we were gone beaver, and I really hadn't planned on dying this way. And that got me mad.

"Well now, mister, I'll tell you," I said, staring hard at the loudmouth who had done the talking so far. "It's been one hell of a spring for me, it really has. I ain't shot a buffalo yet and likely won't. And I've been shot at and beat up more times than I care to recall. And to top it off," I added, giving him the most hateful look I could conjure, "I never did care for mealy-mouthed bastards like you. So if you want to take

243

anything off'n me, plan on it being off my dead body, 'cause you'd never beat me in a fair match."

Flannelmouths never do like to hear the truth about themselves, and this one was no different. If what I'd said didn't put an edge on him, it at least got him mad enough to start thinking about what he'd *like* to do to me instead of what he'd been palavering about a minute ago.

And then there's luck. Or maybe there is some truth about your maker looking after you at times. I figured I'd do a good bit of thinking on that, when I saw Sis standing in the entrance to the store, looking as innocent as ever.

"Excuse me, gentlemen" was all she said, but it was enough to get the three of them to take a quick gander at her as she ducked back out of harm's way. She'd given us the diversion we would need to bring the odds up to even some. Like I said, diversions will kill you if you ain't careful. I say that because it sure did in that loudmouth who'd been threatening me.

Now, I'm not about to tell you that firing the Big Fifty one-handed is an easy feat for any man, but that's what I did. I already had it cocked and was pulling the trigger about the time the barrel was level with the man's elsewheres. The Sharps has one hell of a kick to it, and I did my best to hold it down, but the barrel flew up in the air something fierce as a boom echoed the room. But that Big Fifty had done its job, the slug catching the man high in the chest just below his neckline, sending his thin frame sailing back into the plate glass and shattering the display and the glass as he fell to the boardwalk, dead.

Ira Stone was a few years older than me, but as a marshal, I'd say he had all the gall and determination of Hickok. He wasn't all that fast with a pistol, but once he got it out, he knew how to make it talk. The man he was facing threw a wild shot into Stone's upper chest at the same time the lawman fired high into the gunman's chest. The bullet spun the man around so he faced the boardwalk, and Stone was now ready for a second shot. But he didn't need it, for a shotgun blast from the outside of the store pushed the outlaw back inside, where he fell flat on his back, the better part of his guts spilling to the floor. And if he had a chance to look up at the man in the doorway before he died, he would have seen Fat Jack looking mean as could be as the smoke cleared around him.

While all that was going on, my hat flew

off my head as the third gunman threw a piece of lead my way. I was halfway into reloading that Sharps then, something in the back of my mind telling me that it was probably the last act I'd ever perform on this earth. It was then that two more shots rang out; or maybe I should say they sounded like one shot; they were that close together. They came from my left rear, and as I cocked the Sharps, I glanced over my shoulder to see Colorado Johnny standing by the exit to the back door, that Colt's of his leaking as much gunsmoke as any weapon in the place. And when I looked back, I didn't see the third gunman standing anywhere — he was lying on the floor, dead.

It was then that Asa Turner pulled a pistol from beneath the counter, nervously wavering it back and forth between me and Fat Jack.

"Stand back, all of you!" he said, not sure what it was he would have to do to escape. If that was what he had in mind, he made a big mistake in thinking he could get away with it. Fact is, I do believe he froze like a winter piece of ice when Johnny stuck his own pistol in the base of the man's skull and cocked it.

"You've had a real run of bad luck,

friend," he said, as cool as could be. "Now, if you want to bring it to a right quick end, you just do something besides setting that pistol down real easy. It's your choice."

Actually, Turner didn't have much of a choice at all, because by the time Johnny was talking, I had my Sharps leveled at the store clerk through the crook of my arm and Jack was approaching him from the other side of the counter that separated us, his shotgun hip-level.

"You'd better hurry up and put down that gun, Asa," Jack snarled, "else I'm fixing to unmake you my brother-in-law." Fat Jack must have spent some time with the Army, for he brought the butt of that scattergun up into Turner's side as he dropped his gun, and Turner fell to the floor — in pain. "That's for starters," Jack said.

"You didn't have to do that, you know," Colorado Johnny said as he holstered his own gun.

"Oh, yes I did." Fat Jack gave me a hard, glaring stare as he said, "Old Hard Head here has a tough time believing certain people when they tell him the truth. In this case, I figure I'm gonna have to beat Asa to death before Hooker knows for sure I had nothing to do with this fool's tricks." It was the first time he'd called me Hooker since

I'd met him some years back, and I don't mind telling you it hurt some. Fact is, right then it hurt more than my shoulder did.

"You just leave him be and get me a doctor, Jack, and I'll take care of the law around here," Ira Stone said. His voice was a little shaken, but even with the bleeding he was a tough bird after all. The bullet he'd taken had brought him to his knees, but he was able to make it to his feet once I gave him a hand. He still had a job to do, and, wounded or not, being a lawman was something he'd always be doing as long as he had the strength.

A crowd had begun to gather as a deputy showed up to take Turner to jail, while Fat Jack helped the marshal to the doctor's office. After everyone got their fill of seeing dead bodies and lots of blood on the floor, they went their ways, leaving me and Johnny and Sis, who had made her way through the crowd, alone in the store. There would be time later to get around to explaining myself to Fat Jack, but even if it was all over for everyone else, I still had a few unanswered questions left of my own.

"Isn't he great, Guns?" Sis said, clinging to Colorado Johnny's arm, as full of pride as a woman could be for her man.

"Yeah, he's that, all right." There was no

denying it; the boy had saved our lives with his last-minute shooting. Still, I had to know.

"You mind telling me just where it was you went the day you left Sis alone at Fat Jack's?" Some things you don't beat around the bush about, and this was one of them.

"Why, sure." If Johnny was acting, he was putting on a good show of it for me, looking nearly as innocent now as the girl beside him. "I went over to Fort Dodge to do some more of that checking I was telling you and the marshal about earlier. Why?"

"She says you were gone for a full day and a half, and you and I both know Fort Dodge ain't that far from here."

He shrugged, gave me that disengaging smile he had. "Some things you can't rush. I telegraphed the law in Saint Louis where Turner did his clerking and found out how it was he came on such a large number of jewels to bring here. That was when I found out about the insurance he'd taken out on them, too." Again he shrugged, smiled. "It took 'em a while to gather all the information up for me, but I was there the whole time. You can check."

"Why didn't you do the wiring from right here?"

"Well, Guns, you know how gossipy

people are. I was figuring if I kept most of it a secret, then it wouldn't be so hard to catch Turner if what you were thinking was right. And as it turned out, I'd say for the most part you hit the nail on the head."

"You mean you wouldn't have trusted me to keep my mouth shut with all that *secret* information?" Sis said, sounding a mite hostile.

"Oh, it's not that, Cissy. It's just that . . . well, you know how women are."

Her eyes bulged out, her mouth dropped open about six inches, and I saw fear come into Colorado Johnny's eyes as she started to cuss him out something fierce.

That was when I left, knowing that about-to-be-married folk want some time to themselves.

CHAPTER 19

Ira Stone's wound wasn't all that bad, and Asa Turner did more talking than a trained parrot I once saw back East. Like I figured, Fat Jack got around to speaking to me and we ironed things out, neither one of us having to apologize to the other while we agreed to forget the whole thing. He'd have my business back, and I'd have a saloon to come to in Dodge.

As for Colorado Johnny and Sis, they had a real nice church wedding about a week or so later. I ought to know, because I was there. Yes, yes, I know, I said I never go to those affairs, but there were a couple of things to consider when I was asked to be the best man at this one. One of them was that I couldn't forget Hard Luck Hank's dying words about how Sis was a special woman. Under normal conditions, I reckon I would have agreed to be best man just because of that. But there was a day or two when these kids were talking about getting Fat Jack to stand up for them, and once I heard that, I realized that if Jack ever got to talking to those youngsters about marriage, why, there wouldn't be a wedding at all!

The women set up some fancy little eats after the services, and I made the most of it, sort of like Fat Jack's lunch counter. I was making my way toward the end of a table when I saw Sis standing off to the side, a forlorn look on her face.

"Something wrong?" I asked. I had the feeling that she was about to break out crying.

"I don't know, Guns. It's just that —"

"You're wondering if you did the right thing."

"Yes, something like that." She paused, looking at me in an astonished way. "But how would you . . ."

She let it trail off, and I suddenly realized that I'd said something I had never intended to. It was out of a past I had left behind so many years ago, one I tried to forget. But looking down at her reminded me of Mary, and it crossed my mind that maybe if it would do her some good, it would be worth saying. I set my plate of food down and took her chin softly in my calloused hand.

"Nearly twenty years ago I married a

young girl much like you, Sis. We spent time wondering if we were both doing the right thing before the wedding, but in the end it turned out all that fretting was for nothing."

"Fretting?" She sounded puzzled.

"Sure. We worried about trusting each other so much that we almost forgot how it is you tell what real love is."

"Real love?"

"Yup." I smiled at her, remembering things I hadn't even thought of in years. "When he holds you and you feel as warm inside as his arms make you feel on the outside . . . that's love, Sis."

"Really?"

"Really."

We were silent for a while before she said what I knew she would.

"What happened to her? To your wife?"

"Mary? She was dead a year after we were married." I looked past Sis out the window at the grassy land surrounding us. "It's a hard land, Sis. Mary, she just wasn't hard enough. She was gentle, Mary was."

"I'm sorry."

"Don't be. It was a long time ago. Besides, you're supposed to be happy today."

Johnny walked up then and didn't get out a word before Sis was holding him and kissing him. When she let go, she was smiling, but her eyes were on me instead of on Johnny.

"You're right, Guns, you're right."

Johnny was purely mystified about the whole thing, but Sis was as happy as could be.

"Look," I said, "now that I've gotten you two together, I want you to do me a favor. Give me about ten minutes, and then meet me out back of this hall."

"Sure, Guns, whatever you say," Johnny agreed.

I had my range clothes on and had gotten my horse by the time they came to the rear.

"You're not going now, are you, Guns?"

"Gotta move on. But I got you a present for your wedding. Wanted to give it to you personal." I undid the leather strap around the butt of my Sharps, opened the hidden patch hole, and pulled out the diamond that had been hidden away for what seemed so long a time now. At first I thought Sis was going to faint dead away, looking at it agog the way she did. Being a man, Colorado Johnny was a bit more practical about it all, even if he was as surprised as his new bride.

"Is that the diamond that got stolen?"

I gave them a mischievous smile. "Never can tell. Best way I can think to check it out would be to head on back to Saint Louis and find that jeweler Turner got it from. Tell him you found it after all the excitement had taken place and Turner was in jail, that you wanted to do your civic duty." I winked at Sis. "*That's* when you tell him you just got married and show him Cissy here."

"Huh?"

"I did some telegraphing of my own of late. That gem you're holding is worth a good ten thousand dollars." I reached in my pocket and gave him a sheet of paper. "This is the jeweler's name and address. You tell him you're the fella that found the diamond and mention Matt Hooker to him and he'll give you a thousand-dollar reward for returning it, as well as a ring to fit Cissy's finger."

"Well, thanks, Guns, I really appreciate it," Johnny said, pumping my hand. "But what's this other name? Jim Callahan?"

"Friend of mine who's doing some marshaling up around Ellsworth and Newton. Says he could use a dependable man for a deputy, so I recommended you. Told him you'd be round in a month or so.

"You're a good man, Johnny, good at damn near everything you do. That Mister Odom taught you to have a fine set of principles, and you stand by them. That's important. Now, if you'll get rid of that Colorado Johnny monicker and go back to using your own name . . . well, I've a feeling you'll do well for yourself. Besides, this state's going to need more than just a few good lawmen if the cattle drives keep on coming each summer."

"Oh, Matt," Sis said after kissing me, "I don't know how I'll ever repay you! I'll *never* forget you!"

I set my hat in place and mounted up.

"Giving wasn't made for repaying, Cissy. And I wouldn't worry about me. It's *him* you won't be forgetting."

They gave each other a look, almost a smile before she was kissing him again. When they parted, she had that glow a bride is supposed to have, the one Mary had so long ago.

"You're right, Matt! Oh, you're so right!" Sis said.

"Say, what's going on anyway?" Johnny asked, as puzzled now as he had been the first time she'd said it.

"Don't worry, Son." I smiled at them. "I got a feeling she's gonna let you in on it before the day's out."

Sis blushed blood-red, and Johnny still had that perplexed look about him, and riding off, I had a feeling that seeing them together like that was the only good thing that had happened to me that spring of '74.

ABOUT THE AUTHOR

Jim Miller began his writing career at age ten when his uncle presented him with his first Zane Grey novel. A direct descendant of Leif Erickson and Eric the Red, and a thirteen-year army veteran, Mr. Miller boasts that stories of adventure flow naturally in his blood. His novels to date include *Sunsets* and the Colt Revolver Novels: *Gone to Texas*, *Comanche Trail*, *War Clouds*, *Riding Shotgun*, *Orphans Preferred*, and *Campaigning*. *The Big Fifty* is the first novel in his new series, The Long Guns.

When not busy writing about the future exploits of the Hooker clan, Mr. Miller spends his time ensconced in his 2,000-volume library filled mostly with history texts on the Old West. He lives in Aurora, Colorado, with his wife, Joan, and their two children.

The employees of Thorndike Press hope you have enjoyed this Large Print book. All our Thorndike and Wheeler Large Print titles are designed for easy reading, and all our books are made to last. Other Thorndike Press Large Print books are available at your library, through selected bookstores, or directly from us.

For information about titles, please call:
(800) 223-1244

or visit our Web site at:
www.gale.com/thorndike
www.gale.com/wheeler

To share your comments, please write:
Publisher
Thorndike Press
295 Kennedy Memorial Drive
Waterville, ME 04901